DIETZ

Allison Power of Excellence

1915 - 1990

December 21, 1990

Dear Historical Society Member:

On September 14, 1915, the Indianapolis Speedway Team Company was
founded by James A. Allison. What started as a small company in
Speedway servicing racing cars at the Indianapolis Motor Speedway has
now become two thriving operations under the General Motors umbrella
offering the same standard of quality products and service as Jim
Allison.

Allison's 75-year history is a story of speed, power, and technology.
But the real story is the people--men and women whose energy and
creativity carried Allison through four major wars and produced
generations of new products. In celebration of the 75th anniversary of
Allison Transmission and Allison Gas Turbine Divisions, we are proud to
offer you the Allison story through the enclosed two-volume set
"Allison: Power of Excellence".

We have appreciated the support of Hoosiers across this state throughout
our 75-year history and look forward to a continued partnership in the
future. On behalf of the 20,000 Allison employes and retirees, we hope
you will enjoy the books and share the Allison story with your members
and visitors.

Sincerely,

F. Blake Wallace
VP and General Manager
Allison Gas Turbine Division

Robert M. Clark
General Manager
Allison Transmission Division

Enclosures

Allison Power of Excellence

1915 - 1990

Allison Transmission Division   General Motors Corporation

by   Paul Sonnenburg   &   William A. Schoneberger

Designed by Robaire Ream

Coastline Publishers

*The Allison
75th Anniversary Logo
is the work of ATD marketing
administrator Beatrice Drics.
Ms. Drics holds her B.S. from
Purdue University, and her
design was chosen from 155
entries in the division's
anniversary logo contest.*

Staff for Allison / Power of Excellence
       Allison Transmission Division

Authors: Paul Sonnenburg and William A. Schoneberger

Research: William Campbell, Jack Evans, Dollyne Pettingill, Bruce Roberts,
       Joan Zigmunt
Interviews: William Campbell, Jack Evans, Bruce Roberts, Paul Sonnenburg
Photo Editor: Paul Sonnenburg
Design and Typesetting: Robaire Ream
Production Assistant: Lee Mersini
Printing: Walsworth Publishing Company, Marceline, Missouri

Library of Congress Cataloging in Publication Data
    Sonnenburg, Paul, 1937—
        Allison power of excellence
        Includes index
        1. Allison Transmission Division of General Motors Corporation
    —History. I. Schoneberger, William A. II Title
    Library of Congress Catalog Card Number 90-083437
    ISBN 0-9627074-1-4
Printed in the United States of America
by Walsworth Publishing Company, Marceline, Missouri
First Edition

During its first decade in the transmission business, Allison swiftly dominated the automatic power train market for military tracked vehicles and commercial off-highway applications. By the 1970s the division's AT-MT-HT family of automatics did the same for on-highway vehicles, and the Plant 3 floor sometimes presented vistas like this as hundreds of transmissions awaited shipment.

CONTENTS

For a 75th Anniversary Open House, some 30,000 members of the divisions' extended family gathered at Allison's Indianapolis facilities on September 8, 1990. Fittingly, the senior celebrant was John Goldthwaite, who retired as assistant chief engineer in 1961 after a richly diverse Allison career that began in 1927. The story that follows owes much to this remarkable man.

Preface

Among the events and projects planned for Allison's 75th Anniversary celebrations, none has been more challenging than making our two divisions' illustrated history books.

Our first tasks were to review the company's substantial archives—records, publications, photos, and the rest—and arrange for interviews with current staff and retirees. Then, working with our colleagues at the Gas Turbine Division, came the "rough cut" of material and the choice of the general direction we wished our authors to take.

The Allison story through World War II is dominated for both divisions by the central figures of Jim Allison and the men he chose as associates and employes, notably Carl Fisher and Norman Gilman. Other leading roles in those years were played by two historic aero engines—the Liberty and the V1710—soon followed by Frank Whittle's turbojet. Our first six chapters fittingly focus on these men and machines.

In 1946 destiny urged the Allison organization along two eventually divergent paths. This book traces the route blazed by pioneers in Detroit and Indianapolis as they engineered a whole new industry in power conversion and transmission. Our last chapters examine the accomplishments of their successors who built on solid foundations to create the industry's preeminent enterprise—Allison Transmission Division of General Motors.

With vast material and only 200 pages, we faced lots of hard choices about content. We trust readers will forgive the absence of favorite and undeniably important matters. The makings of several more books await subsequent chroniclers.

Our authors haven't covered it all, certainly, but we hope that members of the Allison family of employes and friends worldwide—past, present, and future—will discover in these pages some of the essence of a great company and its people.

Jack Evans   *Dollyne Pettingill*

Foreword

This volume honors the 75th Anniversary of the Allison Organization and traces the events of a company remarkable for its endurance and exciting because of the application of its products. The events captured and recounted in these pages admirably illustrate the zest and vigor of the people who have made up "Allisons."

Those of us who are part of this history will recognize many familiar names and events, but we will be aware that this is but a sample. We could all contribute to the rest of the story.

Jim Allison told his fledgling organization that "nothing but the best" was to leave the Allison shop. He later instructed the staff to "take the tough jobs, the jobs that others can't do." These basic ideas have served the Allison organization well through the years and are as vital in 1990 and beyond as they were in 1915.

Today Allison is a proud organization, loyal and responsive to our customers, committed to continuous improvement in all that we do. In the rapidly changing business world of 1990, we are changing Allison to maintain our leadership, but we still do "the tough jobs" and we are rededicated to the principle that "nothing but the best" ever leaves an Allison shop.

R.M. Clark

Acknowledgements

The contributions, cooperation, and enthusiastic support of a great many men and women have made this book possible. Division management and staff are joined by our authors, designer, and editors in gratefully recognizing these generous colleagues and friends.

Ressie Abadiano, Larry Allman, Sue G. Amos, Earl Anderson, Wally Anderson, John Arvin, Stephen L. Ashman, Dick Askren, Scott Baier, Andy Bailey, Jack Bailey, James W. Baird, Bryce Baldwin, Jeannette Baldwin, Paul Bancel, Larry Banks, Ray Bannister, Gene Barc, Hill Barrett, William W. Barton, Dan Basehore, Susan M. Bayt, Phillip L. Beam, John Beetham, John Bergman, Donald Beringer, O.H. Billman, David R. Bowling, Tom Brandenberg, Donald N. Brindle, Gus Broffitt, Richard L. Browning, Edward C. Brunes, Bobby C. Bryant , James F. Bumb, Marcia K. Bumb, James Burris, Mel Byers.

Marilyn Campbell, William C. Campbell, Derrell Cannon, John Cartwright, Cecil E. Chaney, Hubert Cheesman, Diana Chenoweth, Tom Ciskowski, Robert M. Clark, Dave Cody, Dick Coffey, Frank M. Coleman, Bill Compton, John Conti, Bob Cook, Edgar R. Cottingham, Morris Crane, Francis E. Crismore, Leo Cuffari, Jack Cummings., Robert J. Curtis, John Custer, Ross Cutler, Len Davidson, Don Davis, Ronald J. Deal, John Debbink, Louis Deck, Bob DePree, Walt DeRoo, Edward H. Dewes, Jim Dietz, Sue Dodds, Dennis Duke, Add Dunn, John Dunn, Dick Duzan, Ken Dye.

Norm Eggers, Richard W. Emmert, W.G. Emmick, Jack R. Evans, Harry Fackenthal, E. Fred Faude, Carol Federspill, Dave Fenwick, Dick Fisher, Mark E. Fisher, Jerry Flanders, John Follmer, Charles W. Fraley., Dan Frankel, Ray Frees, Ken Frost, Gary Fuquay, William L. Gasta, Jack E. Gilbert, Dick Gillum, Samuel E. Golden, John Goldthwaite, Chester G. Good Jr., Dick Goodin, R. Green, D.C. Grey, Dennis Grey, Dallas G. Gritton.

Gregory L. Hadley, James L. Harless, Kenneth B. Harmon, Ralph Hart, Dale A. Hasler, Bob Hatch, Ted Haws, John Hayden, William Heady, Harry Helbig, Gene Helms, Carol A. Henry, Gary Hentrup, Joe Hester, Bob Hicks, Ward Hinds, Frank Hintze, John F. Hittle, Mrs. Gordon Holbrook, Michael W. Holland, Jim Holman, Roger Hooker, Eugene A. Hooper, Bob Hoover, Chuck Hoover, Michael Horton, Dick Hoyt, Mike Hudson, Albert C. Huevel, Bill Hutson, Regina Jackson, Dan Jacobsen, John Jacox, Harlan Jobes.

Reta J. Kaiser, Herb Karsch, Tony Kennington, Bob Keough, John Kirkpatrick, John Kistler, Johnny Kline, Jim Knott, Henry Korte, Eric Krueger, Dick Kurzawa, Jack Kurzawa, Charles R. Lammert, Steve LaMotte, Bud Lander, John Latcovich, Harry E. Latshaw, Don R. Laughlin, Harold Leahy, Lowell N. Legge, Ruby Lester, William H. Lindley, John Lingeman, Whitey Lingeman, Tim Long, Howard Lord, Frank Losonsky, Jay Lotz, Lawrence A. Love, Bob Lowry, Jim Lunsford, Eric F. Lutz.

Raymond J. Maci, Earnie Mackey Jr., Phil Malone, W. Maple, R. Keith Martin, Albert Maxwell, Jim Mayfield, George Mayo, Gloria McCallister, John J. McCardle,

John H. McDonald, Matthew J. McGloine, Wayne McIntire, Dick McKenna,
Linda A. McMann, Denise McNamara, Carl McNeely, Fritz Medenwald,
Nick Meko, Charles D. Mendenhall, Carlisle L. Miles, David L. Miller, Barry Miller,
Betty Miller, Jack Mitchell, Larry Mitchell, James A. Mitchner, Don Moench,
Al Morjig, Glenn A. Morris, Donald Morrison, Dean Mosser, Roger Mosser,
David E. Motter, Dale F. Mueller, Jerry W. Munk.

Buzz Neate, Stan Nelson, Dave Newill, John Newkirk, Jerry Niemann,
Kurt Niemann, Michael W. Nigh., Dan Nigro, Al Novick, Med C. Obery II,
Dave Oeth, Leon E. Onken, James P. Ordo, Richard A. Ordo, Don Orme,
Theodore W. Orth, Bob Owens, Phil Painter, Lois Paul, Richard Paul,
George Pederson, Tony Perona, Clarence Perry, Sid Perry, Dollyne W. Pettingill,
Lonnie Pham, Carl Pieper, Richard Pierson, James C. Polak, Dave Power,
Dave Quick.

Diane Raflo, Steve Rainey, Carol S. Rasp, James R. Ray, Marv Recht, Bob Reed,
J.R. Reed, Katherine Reed, Bill Richardson, Wayne Ricks, Robert M. Rider,
Ross Rigby, Barb Riggs, Larry Ritter, Anita S. Roberts, Bruce M. Roberts,
Mrs. Horace Roberts, C. Rockwood, Xavier Romero, Paul Rose, Bob Roth,
Kaye Rush, Hugh Sample, Paul Sappenfield, Bill Sare, Judith S. Satchel,
Jim Sauer, Richard E. Sauer, Robert M. Schaefer, Ralph N. Scheidt, Rick Schenkel,
Albert R. Schuette, Carl Settles, Scott Shadwick, Noble Shepherd, Rex Shields,
Donna J. Shirley, Ed Sickmeier, John Siegrist, Verna R. Slyder, Carolyn Smith,
Donald Smith, G. Smith, O.P. Smith, Sidney O. Smock, Al Sobey, David South,
Bill Sparks, Paul Sparks, Bob Spoon, Bill Springer, Eloy Stevens, Max E. Stewart,
R.J. Stewart, John E. Storer, Mary Stowers, Edward L. Such, Dave Sulkoske,
Chris Swain, Jon Swanson, William T. Swift.

Fred Tangman, Glen L. Taylor, John M. Taylor, Bill Thomas, C.H. Thomas,
Angus Thompson, Rob Titlow, Luke Trice, Patzetta M. Trice, Betty S. Truax,
Joe Turner, Larry Van Buskirk, Gene Van Cleve, Marilyn Vandeventer,
Janet B. Vaughn, Frank Verkamp, Daniel R. Voss., Gene Wade, Chuck Wagner,
Blake Wallace, Frank Walters, Floyd Waters, Johnny Watson, Robert A. Weakley,
Jennifer D. Weaver, Harvey Welch, Richard E. Welsh, Bob Wente, John Wheatley,
Jay W. White, John Whitmore, John R. Wiley, Warren Wilkes, Jim Willeford,
Wanda Willis, Thomas E. Winter, Roger D. Wisecup, Lowell Woodard,
Floyd E. Workman, Donald R. Wright, Joan Zigmunt, Donald G. Zimmerman,
Bev Zolezzi.

Special thanks also to: the Department of Oral History at Indiana University,
Bloomington; the Indianapolis Motor Speedway Museum; the public relations
staffs and archivists at GM Headquarters in Detroit, Lockheed in Burbank, and
General Dynamics in San Diego; the Information Officers at the U.S. Navy in
Los Angeles; the U.S. Army at Fort Rucker, Fort Knox, and Aberdeen Proving
Ground; and the Business History Collection, University of California at
Los Angeles.

CHAPTER 1
Preparing

James Allison, family, background, and career to 1917; personal qualities, attitude, associates.
Beginnings, development, key people, operation of predecessor companies; Carl Fisher,
P.C. Avery and the Concentrated Acetylene Company; Prest-O-Lite; The Speedway; Indianapolis Speedway Team Company.

Previous page: Even in the ritual of a formal 1920s portrait some of the attributes noted by the contemporaries of Jim Allison are evident: unassuming confidence and poise, intelligence, determination, and the suggestion of an impending smile.

E xcellence is a word often abused in today's culture and commerce. However, few corporate organizations can be so aptly said to exemplify the word's authentic meaning as the Allison divisions of General Motors. The accomplishments of the men and women of these unique enterprises, from the outset of the Allison companies 75 years ago, endure as proof of their dedication to genuine excellence.

This notion of excellence, the concept of quality and a dedication to doing the job right, are documented in the illustrious history and heritage of Allison that began with one man's devotion to doing worthwhile things superbly.

James Ashbury Allison

Often as significant as a man's measurable accomplishment is his contemporary reputation, particularly for achievers of Jim Allison's stature. Certain Allison characteristics recur consistently in the observations of his friends and colleagues. He was genuinely admired by his business associates. He had an instinct for business opportunity, and the perseverance to support his plans. He worked harmoniously with others. He was regarded as providing the balance and organization for enterprises that sometimes began as dreams. But the success of those enterprises appears directly linked to his aptitude for practical business as well as a capacity for intense concentration on whatever venture claimed his interest. Moreover, a single thread runs through this legend: Jim Allison's passion for quality.

The Allison Family in Indiana

In October 1967 amateur historian John W. Kirkpatrick presented a slide show at a meeting of the GM Regalers Club that he titled "Jim Allison & Friends." From Kirkpatrick's narrative, portions of this introduction to Jim Allison are freely adapted.

The Allison family arrived in Indiana in 1840. Born in England, James M. Allison brought his Scots bride Julia to the Indiana frontier and was soon established in Greene County, say local records, as a Worthington businessman of property who owned a fleet of river boats that plied between Worthington and Louisville, Kentucky. The rivers were then the only highways into an unknown land, linking the first settlements, providing power for mills and industry, and bearing the commerce of goods and ideas.

The couple's son Noah was born in 1846, and when the boy was 12, the family moved to Hillsdale, Michigan. There the father earned local prominence, apparently as a wholesale grocer. Noah was educated in Hillsdale, grew to manhood, and joined his father's business as a salesman, traveling in Pennsylvania. In 1870 he married and moved to Marcellus, Michigan, where, in August 1872, his second son, James Ashbury Allison, was born. In 1874 the family returned to Indiana, moving to South Bend, and then in 1880, to Indianapolis. Noah Allison had been a traveling agent for the National Surgical Institute and in 1882 he joined with Benjamin Nixon to form a knitting and hosiery manufacturing company, Allison & Nixon. In 1883 he and his brothers formed the Allison Knitting Company.

Noah Allison's Coupons

In 1885 Noah Allison launched a new phase of his career, one displaying some of the innovation and uncommon determination that would later serve his son so well. As America's consumer economy grew increasingly complex, retail business was often done on credit. Many debtors could not, or would not, pay their debts. So Noah Allison and George W. Abell organized the American Creditors Association.

Two years later Allison was president of the business, and apparently ready for new challenges. In 1888 Indianapolis was a thriving center of regional business and trade. Didn't the city need a trade publication? Certainly. So Noah Allison, experienced and observant businessman and articulate writer, saw another opportunity for his talents—in the world of publishing. He moved his collections company to more spacious quarters and simultaneously began to edit and publish the *Indiana Trade Review*. Like most newspaper operations of the era, the *Review's* equipment lent itself to job printing and bookbinding. But Noah was not like most other editor-publishers. He found another angle.

Noah Allison had helped merchants collect their receivables. Now he conceived a profitable way to help the debtors. Since his wholesale grocery days when he worked with his father, Noah was keenly aware of how poorly many men handled their money, drinking and gambling it away on payday.

Noah initiated a system among local merchants so that many necessary commodities could be paid for with scrip instead of cash. On payday a man would buy booklets with coupons good only for, say, groceries at a certain store, and valid only when detached by the grocery store clerk.

Buying a coupon book at a small discount, a man could get more groceries than if he used cash. The grocers did cash business and got their money in advance. All over the country retailers, mine and mill operators, and company stores clamored for coupon books. The ink and paper suppliers barely kept up with the demand at Allison Coupon. Noah brought his three oldest sons into the business and moved to bigger quarters in 1890.

But Noah Allison was not to enjoy the fruits of his prospering business. With his untimely death that very year, his wife, Myra, became proprietor of Allison Coupon and the three oldest sons—Wallace, James, and Dillmore—became directors. Placed under the management of prominent Indianapolis attorney John Berryhill, the company prospered and grew, moving to larger quarters five times in ten years, finally locating in 1904 on East Market, with Berryhill as president, James A. Allison, vice president, Wallace S. Allison, secretary, and Dillmore C. Allison, superintendent.

Workmen building the Panama Canal between 1904 and 1914 were paid in part with Allison coupon books. In Army posts nationwide the familiar perforations snapped steadily every payday. America's very first installment loans, in 1919, were repaid using Allison loan coupon books. And with appropriate coincidence, in 1922 General Motors Acceptance Corporation began using Allison payment books.

The children and grandchildren of Noah Allison operated the business until 1963 when it was sold to the Cummins-American Corporation.

Partners in Fortune

But, having married childhood sweetheart Sarah in 1907 (the marriage would end in divorce in June 1928), Jim Allison was destined for grander things than credit coupons. If destiny did smile on the young coupon company vice president in 1904, it can hardly have found a more apt bearer than Jim Allison's lifetime friend and soon-to-be partner, Carl Graham Fisher, the

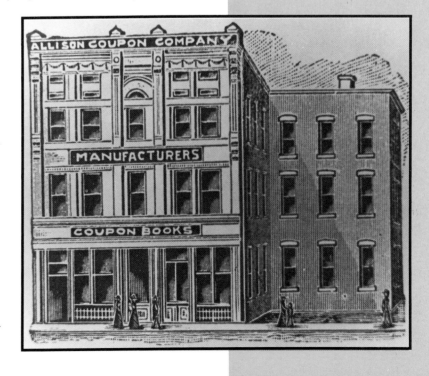

Founded by Jim Allison's father Noah in 1885, the Allison Coupon Company of Indianapolis was operated by family members until its sale in 1963. This engraving of the home office was made in 1896.

"Fabulous Hoosier." Born in Greensburg, Indiana, Carl Fisher came to Indianapolis as a boy. He soon earned a name as a showman and promoter whose zany schemes were often shrewd and sensible. Like bicycles.

The penny-farthing high wheel bicycle, a common means of transport, was as mechanically fragile as it was awkward to mount. To Fisher that meant a bicycle repair shop. When the less colorful but far sturdier modern "Safety Bicycle" was invented, Fisher wasted no time arranging local sales franchises for several makes, and even one national franchise. With showy promotions and advertising, he built a mammoth bicycle business.

But Carl Fisher's interest in bicycles was soon overtaken by the motorcar. Launching into the auto sales business, Fisher used his sales savvy to profitable effect. By 1904 "Crazy Carl" was so busy with his prosperous automobile agency that he was difficult to catch up to. At least it seemed that way to Percy Avery who had called several times at the Fisher Automobile Co. trying to make an appointment. Finally, one day when Fisher was late for lunch, Avery managed to catch him and state his business.

Among other irksome and awkward equipment, early autos came equipped with kerosene lamps, only nominally superior to darkness. Newer models featured lights that burned acetylene from a generator

An imaginative and extraordinarily able entrepreneur whose career included major contributions in Indiana and South Florida, Carl Fisher was among Jim Allison's closest friends. The two collaborated in successful business ventures, including founding of the Speedway, from 1904 until Allison's untimely death in 1928.
Courtesy, Indy 500 Photos

that dripped water into a container of calcium carbide on the running board, creating illumination and annoyance in roughly equal measure. Percy Avery had an idea for compressing and storing a quantity of acetylene in a small steel cylinder. Even as Avery spoke, Fisher's canny mind was outlining a new venture. Hurrying Avery along to lunch, Fisher envisioned a business that would serve the whole automobile industry. All they needed was someone to put up the money.

And who was Carl meeting for lunch? None other than his good friend Jim Allison. Through the front window glass at Pop Haynes Restaurant, passersby might have witnessed some enthusiastically expansive gestures. Allison had to borrow part of the money, but in September 1904 Carl G. Fisher, James A. Allison, and Percy C. Avery formed the Concentrated Acetylene Co. with capital stock of $10,000. Offices were in Fisher's Automobile Agency on North Illinois.

By November they'd built a small plant at 28th and Pennsylvania and the business of concentrating acetylene got under way. Folks agreed it was Fisher's craziest venture yet. Everyone knew that compressed acetylene explodes with fearsome violence. They were right, of course, but Carl was unperturbed by the regular disasters at the Concentrated Acetylene Co. There was tremendous demand for compressed acetylene.

The Proof Is in the Racing

At the Indiana State Fair car races in Indianapolis in 1905, a festive Labor Day crowd cheered a victorious Barney Oldfield across the finish line in his Green Dragon. In the stands Carl Fisher and Jim Allison had been joined by some friends in the now-expanding Indianapolis automotive community: Frank Wheeler of Wheeler-Schebler Carburetor Company, Harry C. Stutz of Stutz Automobile fame, and Arthur Newby, principal owner of National Motor Car and Vehicle Corporation of Indianapolis.

Charles Merz drove one National racer, Jap Clemens the other, to smash world records held by the French Renaults. Supervising pit work for National was 26-year-old Norman H. Gilman, assistant to the superintendent of Newby's firm.

America's mounting fascination with the automobile may have been no keener anywhere than in this heartland of the nation. Allison's friends had each made strong commitments to the motor car that was fast becoming an immensely appealing consumer product. Together they were uniquely qualified to enhance the infant automobile industry's potential. Caught up in the zest of the competition, Allison and Fisher and their friends decided that day to arrange a 24-hour race to be held on the same track later in the year. Fisher naturally suggested that they light the track with acetylene lamps for night driving.

Jim Allison was chosen to manage the rousingly successful November affair. In a spirit of cooperation to advance American cars, automobile men from all around the nation came. New records were set, including raising the 24-hour distance mark from 789 to 1,094 miles.

The Indianapolis Motor Speedway

In the early hours of that November morning, someone, perhaps Fisher, said: "We ought to have a real paved and banked track with two-and-a-half mile laps. Then we'd hang up some real records." The friends not only agreed, but set in motion the historic wheels of the world's best-known and most enduring auto racing competition. In 1909 Allison, Fisher, Newby, and Wheeler founded the Motor Speedway after spending $72,000 for farmland. Jim Allison's real estate broker Lemuel (Lem) Trotter handled the deal. When the speedway was built, Allison was

secretary-treasurer of the firm and became president just after the 1923 race. He continued in that position until the project was taken over by Edward V. Rickenbacker and his associates in 1926.

The first race was held in 1909, and the first Indianapolis Speedway 500-Mile International Sweepstakes Race was run on May 30, 1911. From its beginnings, the race transcended mere sporting entertainment.

The gala event provided a common meeting ground for auto designers, engineers, manufacturers, and the world's premier racing drivers.

Ray Harroun, driving a Marmon, won the 1911 race; Joe Dawson won in 1912 with a National car, aided by his partner, Johnny Aitken. In the 1913 race as many foreign cars as American competed. But Arthur Newby's National was not entered, even though it had won 80 of 81 races that year. Newby, having gotten plenty of advertising, was tired of racing. Some thought the Peugeot's Indy victory due in part to help from 24-year-old Johnny Aitken who, with no National cars to race, had lent a hand to the French team.

Meanwhile, Back at the Gasworks

In March 1906 Fisher and Allison had moved their acetylene operations to a larger facility on South East Street. After Percy Avery left the organization, Fisher and Allison changed its name to Prest-O-Lite Company. Expansion prompted a series of moves to increasingly larger plants—East South Street, Oliver Avenue, and South Meridian. By 1911 the explosions abated and business continued to prosper.

Jim Allison felt sufficiently confident to begin construction of an elegant new residence that year, one of many projects that exemplified his determination to be associated with nothing but the highest quality. During the two years needed to build his Riverdale estate, Allison engaged renowned architects, builders, and artisans with instructions to create the finest structure possible. Complementing various exotic woods was white marble brought from Italy, and each major room was decorated in a different motif.

Coincidentally, in September 1912, at a cost just over a half million dollars, Prest-O-Lite completed a new plant of nearly 300,000 sq. ft. on land adjacent to the Speedway track.

A Track, a Race, a Team

John Aitken's friendship with Jim Allison offers a clue to origins of the Speedway and the Allison Company. Aitken approached Allison with the suggestion that Jim start a racing team. Allison was

Facing, top: Obviously pleased with themselves and their new racetrack on opening day in 1909, the four founders of the Indianapolis Motor Speedway posed with their distinguished guest from Detroit. Left to right, Henry Ford, Arthur Newby, Frank Wheeler, Carl Fisher, and Jim Allison.

Facing, bottom: Launching what would become one of the world's great sporting events, drivers cross the starting line of the first Indianapolis Speedway 500-Mile International Sweepstakes Race, May 30, 1911. The clouds of white smoke are caused by castor oil added to the fuel to improve cylinder-wall lubrication. Courtesy, Indy 500 Photos

Below, left: With the camera angle making his big Marmon appear to lean into the wind, Ray Harroun heads for victory in the first Indy 500. Harroun was widely regarded as an able engineer and car designer as well as a winning driver. Courtesy, Indy 500 Photos

Above: Begun in 1911 and requiring two years to complete, Jim Allison's spacious Riverdale home combined tasteful architecture, luxurious materials, and superb craftsmanship. The designer's generous use of glass fills the home with cascades of light and views of the rolling site.

Each of the principal rooms at Riverdale featured a distinctive decorating motif. The Sun Room, filled with tropical plants and furnished with rattan and bamboo furniture whose cushions were covered with bright floral print, evoked the Far East.

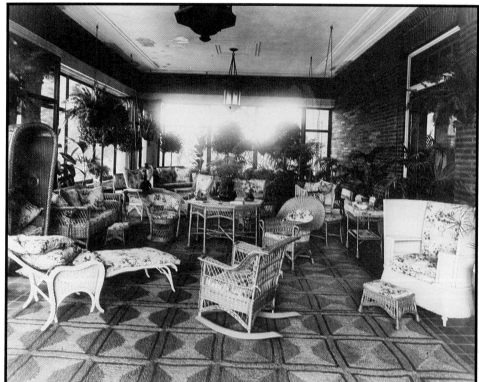

intrigued. He apparently had little trouble enlisting enthusiastic agreement from his friends Fisher, Wheeler, and Newby. Accustomed to personal success and borne forward by rising national and regional optimism, Jim Allison and his comrades eagerly took up the new challenge implicit in Aitken's urgent wish to race again. They quickly assembled three racing teams, starting with the Indianapolis Speedway Team Company. The founding date of this company that would one day emerge as the Allison divisions of General Motors is September 14, 1915.

Below: Luxuriant in cool marble and elegant palms, Riverdale's Aviary glowed with sunshine and the opulence of a Moroccan palace. Persian rugs graced the marble floor around the crystal-fountained pool.

Below: John Aitken, shown here before the 1911 Indy, in 1915 urged Jim Allison to form a racing team. In part at Aitken's suggestion, Allison and his partners formed the Indianapolis Speedway Team Company. Aitken was named manager, chief engineer, and ranking driver. Courtesy, Indy 500 Photos

Not unexpectedly, its manager, chief engineer, and ranking driver was irrepressible Johnny Aitken.

Indy Successes and a Man Named Eddie

Successful driver Ray Harroun was also a talented engineer who designed his own racer and persuaded the Maxwell Motor Car Company to build it. Allison and Fisher sponsored the necessary team, calling it the Prest-O-Lite team. And, making his first appearance in the Allison story, "colorful Eddie Rickenbacker, 'heavy-footed go-like-hell-till-bust,' who never won a race because he burned up his cars before finishing," was hired to manage the team and be its lead driver. In years to come, the aggressive young Rickenbacker would more than once play a fateful role in the Allison corporate drama.

The First Shops

Under the banner of their Indianapolis Speedway Team Company, Allison and Fisher put up a shop in a rented building on Georgia Street in downtown Indianapolis. Here they redesigned and rebuilt domestic and foreign cars for the races, including a fleet of Peugeot racers bought by Allison. For two years they were unsuccessful. Late in 1916 a somewhat discouraged Allison said, "Let's quit fooling around. This thing of running the cars out on the track for testing and then running them back to the shop three miles away is a nuisance and inefficient. Let me take over the company and I'll build a real shop out near the Speedway where it will be convenient." All agreed, and Allison became sole owner of the Indianapolis Speedway Team Company, while Fisher retained the Prest-O-Lite team. The little shop near the track was built, staffed with the finest craftsmen, and equipped with the best tools obtainable.

Norman Gilman Joins Allison

In December 1916 Allison and Aitken talked about finding a replacement for their shop superintendent who had quit. Coincidentally, John Aitken's friend Norman Gilman had just submitted his resignation as assistant superintendent at National Motors. One evening before Christmas, Gilman met with Jim Allison at Riverdale. The meeting would ultimately meld one man's passion for quality with another's practical vision.

On January 1, 1917, Norman H. Gilman became chief engineer and superintendent of the Allison Speedway Team Company. Aitken moved up to vice president and general manager. Allison remained president of the 20-man operation.

In that same year, 34 Prest-O-Lite branch plants were in operation. Fisher and Allison were already millionaires. They sold the 30,000-share

Surrounded by the paraphernalia of Allison's busy shop in Plant 1 on Main Street, shop superintendent C.L. Trosky, far left, confers with a colleague in April 1920.

Howdy Wilcox drove his Allison-commissioned and meticulously re-worked Peugeot to victory in the 1919 Indy, the last race in which Jim Allison's team would participate. Allison sold his cars and began his Florida development work while the engineering company sharpened its focus on aviation engine technology.

controlling interest in Prest-O-Lite for $9,000,000, but Allison retained large blocks of Prest-O-Lite and Union Carbide & Carbon stock.

A Nucleus Evolves

With Indianapolis a beacon for racing car drivers from everywhere, the shop of the Allison Speedway Team Company soon became a recognized center not only for pre-race honing of thoroughbred race cars, but also for the day-to-day business of refining the modern automobile. Here top mechanics explored pioneering designs and precision manufacturing problems for the following year's entrants.

But pervading the shop's operation on the corner of the Prest-O-Lite lot was James Allison the perfectionist, constantly demanding something new, something challenging, never satisfied with things as they were. No project or policy remained uninfluenced by his wide-ranging intelligence, judgment, careful preparation, dignity, and quiet manner. One observer overheard Jim tell a workman, "I want you to remember that this is not just another machine shop. Whatever leaves this shop over my name must be the finest work possible." That statement was his creed.

The First World War Comes to Speedway

With their best-available tools and equipment, the shop staff worked on new race car designs and models under the direction of Aitken and shop superintendent C.L. Trosky, while secretary and treasurer Luther Langston tended to financial and administrative matters. But on April 17, 1917, the morning after America declared war against Germany, Allison gathered his crew and said, "Quit work on the cars, but keep our men and continue to pay them."

Unable to reach Fisher or Newby, Allison phoned the newspapers to tell them there would be no more races until the war was over. Then he turned to Gilman and said, "Go find out how we can get war orders rolling. Take any jobs you like, especially the ones other fellows can't do, anything that will help us get started. Don't figure costs or wait to quote prices. We'll take care of that later." Indeed they would, and with Norman Gilman's leadership and a new name—Allison Experimental Company—Jim Allison's fledgling firm would soon begin making its way in the world.

Jim Allison and Florida

Having given his team its charter and the resources for its accomplishment, Jim Allison would wield his influence from a distance.

After the war ended, Allison commissioned a winning car for the 1919 Indy, then abandoned racing and sold all his cars to aviatrix Ruth Law, who used them in barnstorming and exhibition work.

Jim Allison, in association with Carl Fisher, then began a second phase of extraordinary achievement, in Florida real estate industries. He built an aquarium in Miami whose collection of marine fishes earned worldwide distinction. He also built a hospital in North Miami Beach. Active in the city's civic and business life, genial Jim Allison soon became one of the most widely known winter residents of Miami Beach. His large and handsome home on Biscayne Bay's Star Island became a meeting place for sportsmen, captains of industry, and celebrities. A director of the First National Bank of Miami Beach and principal owner of the Miami Ocean View Company, Allison worked closely with his friend Carl Fisher to spearhead the development of South Florida.

A Life of Its Own

Certainly the company's roots lay in the advent of the motor car. But almost from inception, the process of exploring new avenues that led to dependability, speed, efficiency, and utility steered the Allison group toward imaginative technical solutions and bold approaches to fundamental use of power—its generation, its control, its full range of possibility. Just as it would forever alter the nation's perspective of the world, the first World War brought the first glimmer of potential greatness to Jim Allison's tiny enterprise next door to the Speedway. That potential was unprepossessing enough, contained as it was in a set of drawings hastily executed over five feverish days in a Washington, D.C., hotel room.

The 1919 Indy field prepares for the start of the first race following the 500's wartime suspension. Courtesy, Indy 500 Photos

OFFICIAL
SPEEDWAY PHOTO
No 10839

CHAPTER 2
Emerging

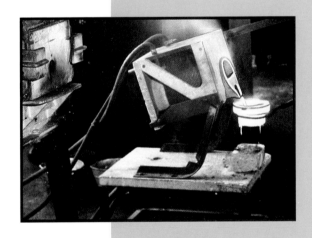

*Allison Experimental Company,
its people, its character, its place in
Indianapolis. The military
establishment, World War I;
the Liberty engine. Gears, bearings,
diversification; Rolls, Wright, and other
customers.
Allison Engineering; Norman Gilman
and the search for a core product.
Death of Jim Allison.*

*"The vaunted Liberty." This
model, manufactured by the
Allison Engineering
Company during WWI, bears
the Allison logo on the
reduction gear cover. The
large, flanged boss
surrounding the geared shaft
allowed its eight through-
bolts to evenly distribute
clamping forces on the big
wooden, fixed-pitch
propellers commonly fitted to
the V-12 engines.*

Allison's historical links to American aeronautical and vehicular development assured the company its early place at the forefront of two industries to which it continues to make touchstone contributions.

In the four years preceding World War I, Jim Allison's wealth permitted him to pursue his interests in the vanguard of automotive development. He assembled a cadre of imaginative engineers and mechanics and provided them with quality tools, equipment, and facilities. American industrial development was changed forever when Europe was plunged into World War I. Overnight the carefree cheering for swift new race cars in Speedway faded. From London and Paris came a clamor for swift new warplanes for the recently-developing art of aerial warfare. The outbreak of the Great War meant aero engines, lots of aero engines.

Anxious men in cities not so distant from Indianapolis were soon developing a powerplant that would profoundly influence American aviation and give Allison's little company its steppingstone to international distinction.

The Curious Origins of a Hasty Hybrid

Even as Prest-O-Lite had been rising from the noise of its first years in Speedway to light the auto driver's way and generate the capital that funded the Allison Speedway Team Company, in Ohio the motorcar was being further sophisticated. In Dayton, home of the Wright brothers and the powerful National Cash Register Company, NCR vice president and chief engineer Edward Deeds hired a young fellow named Charles Kettering from Ohio State University to electrify the cash register.

Kettering had observed that a small electric motor could carry a huge load for short periods—nifty for adding machines and coincidentally providing a welcome relief for weary motorists who had to "get out and crank" to get their auto engines turning when Deeds applied Kettering's idea to auto starters. In 1908 he and Kettering formed Dayton Engineering Laboratories Company (Delco) to build electric starters, introduced on 1912 Cadillacs. Deeds next designed the first eight-cylinder car, the 1914 Cadillac. From this modest beginning Kettering launched an unparalleled career with GM that would repeatedly touch Allison fortunes.

Edward Deeds remained interested in cars and motors and, when World War I erupted, he joined Kettering and dam designer Harold Talbott to organize the Dayton-Wright Company, with Orville Wright as vice president and consultant. When the U.S. declared war, Deeds went to Washington as a member of the Aircraft Production board, of which Hudson Motor Car Company's Howard Coffin was chairman.

With a $640 million appropriation, the board drew up a plan to deliver 50,000 airplanes to France in one year's time. Put in charge of aircraft procurement, Deeds decided that aircraft development efforts should focus

on a single engine. Legend has it that he locked two auto engineers in a Washington hotel room and in five days they produced a design that would become the historic Liberty engine.

"The engine," writes aviation historian Carl Solberg, "had automobile stamped all over it—eight cylinders, water-cooled, a Delco battery instead of magnetos." Redesigned with 12 cylinders like Britain's Rolls-Royce and reworked yet again, it passed into high volume production as America's principal aero contribution to the Allied war effort.

Doing the Necessary

Jim Allison's prompt commitment of his shop resources to war production quickly launched a flow of challenging design and manufacturing jobs, including high speed crawler-type tractors for hauling artillery and battlefield equipment, Whippet tanks, tank tracks, and production superchargers. The staff grew to 50, then 100, plus a temporary complement of 150 draftsmen to create and coordinate the reams of drawings needed to insure that parts built from them would work together. Production workers routinely logged 60- and 100-hour weeks.

But of all the projects, the most significant came from the Nordyke & Marmon Motor Company, who had government contracts to build both Hall-Scott engines and Liberties. Interchangeable manufacture in those days

Someone once asserted that aircraft engines are made up of equal parts of metal, sweat, and paper. From drafting rooms similar to this one in Speedway c. 1922, flowed the acres of drawings needed to accomplish engine design and rework during WWI.

Among the diverse war machines built under contract by Allison between 1915 and 1918 was a Caterpillar-type half-track field support vehicle.

required a complete, meticulously precise master model that became the standard against which factory-made parts were measured. Allison constructed two master model Liberties from Production Board drawings, together with a full set of tools, jigs, dies, fixtures, and gauges. By war's end Allison had also built several hundred Liberty engines in-house. Ultimately, 20,478 were produced by a wide range of U.S. engine makers. Perhaps 10,000 reached Europe. On Armistice Day 1918 the remainder lay in shipping crates at Wright Field.

Probably not featured on recruiting posters was this WWI tracked, gun-carrying vehicle, typical of the military contract work undertaken in the Allison shops in Speedway during the First World War.

Among licensed manufacturers of Liberty motors was Nordyke & Marmon. This device, engraved in four colors, emblazoned certificates presented to employees in December 1918 when the company was honored by the Bureau of Aircraft Production. In October the plant had turned out 308 engines, 246 percent over their quota of 125.

NORDYKE & MARMON COMPANY
ESTABLISHED 1851
INDIANAPOLIS, IND., U.S.A.

The Allison Twelve

Wartime work, particularly with the Liberty engine, had challenged the Allison people. They were eager for fresh opportunities. Throughout the 1920s Gilman and his staff steadily shaped the company's mastery of high performance engine technology and the parallel challenge of transmitting power into propulsion. Projects ranged from indulgent and futuristic to daring and standard-setting, but each deepened the Allison pool of knowledge and skills.

Among the special pleasures of Jim Allison and his affluent friends were big boats and yachts. Carl Fisher, for example, used his 80-foot *Sea Horse* to commute from his Long Island estate to his Manhattan offices and for seasonal voyages between New York and Miami.

When Allison acquired his 72-foot *Altonia II* soon after the war, he found no satisfactory marine engine of the needed size on the market. He asked Gilman to set about building an engine worthy of the Allison name. Reviewing final specifications with his employer, Gilman objected that they could not make a profit on such engines. Replied Allison, "Norman, we're not running a job shop for profit. Your job is to build the best engine possible." And so they did, announcing in 1920 the Allison Twelve marine engine. Derived from the Liberty, but much refined and more robust, it was intentionally heavy, with cast-iron cylinders instead of welded steel and a massive manganese- bronze crankcase-bedplate. Finished with the precision of an aircraft engine, it was completely waterproof, unprecedentedly smooth and quiet, generated 425 hp at 1,500 rpm, and was priced at $25,000. Offered as an accessory for the large engine was the Allison Lite, a four-kilowatt power set with a GE generator driven by an unusually compact and quiet 500-lb. Allison four-cylinder L-head gasoline engine.

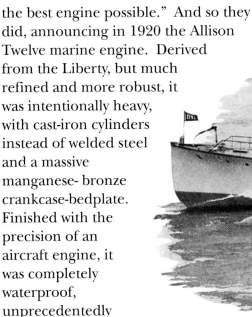

In gray enamel, gleaming bronze, and sparkling nickel plate, the 4,400-pound masterpieces were given almost reverent treatment on their trip to the fitting-out basin. A dozen were produced: four for Allison, two for Arthur Newby, two for Carl Fisher, and four to sell. Fitted with her twin Twelves, *Sea Horse* could achieve 26 knots, *Altonia II,* 30. In their years of service on the Atlantic, the engines performed faultlessly, becoming a legend among East Coast yachtsmen.

The Gilman Bearing

The surplus Liberties stored in Dayton warehouses, however, were not so reliable. While they boasted modern engineering, with crankshaft and connecting rods of heat-treated alloy steel, and tungsten-steel exhaust valves, they also shared with most of that era's aero engines a grave shortcoming: crankshaft and connecting rod bearings that routinely failed after only

Carl Fisher's 80-ft. **Sea Horse,** *fitted with a pair of Allison Twelve marine engines in 1920, sizzled along at a flank speed of 26 knots. Fisher used the yacht to commute from his Long Island mansion to downtown Manhattan and in Miami.*

Arrayed c. 1920 are five machines that helped to establish Allison's reputation for quality. On the floor are a precision reduction-gear assembly for the Liberty and a V-drive marine gear that allowed a level-mounted engine to drive an angled propshaft in a compact hull installation. On stands are the four-cylinder Allison Lite generator set, a Liberty, and the Allison Twelve marine engine.

Something of an indulgence, only a dozen Allison Twelve marine engines were built, for the yachts of Allison and his friends. Adapted from the Liberty design and priced at $25,000, the 425-hp engines became famous for their reliability and durability.

The Allison hallmark stamped on a part or cast into the coverplate on an engine became synonymous with excellence.

An inventive engineer and manager, Norman Gilman not only handled the day-to-day operations of the company during its early phases as general manager and chief engineer, but assured its future success by developing the steel-backed bearing and tirelessly pursuing conception and development of the V1710 engine from 1927 until his retirement in 1936.

about 50 hours. Whether in service or during upgrading tests at Allison, this flaw continued to nag. One engine, for example, was rebuilt and fueled with 20% benzol to increase horsepower from 450 to 500 only to thrash its bearings to junk in 31 hours, a noisy disappointment repeated with engine after engine. Not inappropriately, it was Norman Gilman's analysis and insight that led to a fix for the Liberty and a new product line for Allison.

In the Liberty's connecting rod design, the bearing rigidly clamped into a forked rod worked laterally on the outside of a bronze shell that distorted out-of-round under heavy engine loads. With dimensional stability lost and stresses no longer distributed uniformly, the bearing simply disintegrated, usually sooner rather than later. Gilman calculated that a steel shell, with twice the strength and three times the stiffness of bronze, would adequately resist distortion. To make the shell itself was straightforward, but to obtain the needed soft metal bearing surface on its outside proved more complex. Extensive experiments led to heating the steel form to a bright red and casting molten lead-bronze around it, then machining the cooled bearing surface to fit. The process was a complete success and extended the Liberty's service life from tens to hundreds of hours.

One result was a series of Army contracts to retrofit new bearings to surplus Liberties, usually in lots of 1,000. One 1928 Liberty contract totalled $1 million. More important, the superior bearing technology provided spectacular performance improvement in newer powerplant designs, and soon Allison was supplying bearings to engine makers worldwide. For the Wright Aeronautical Company's Whirlwind engine, they made bearings with the bronze on the inside instead of the outside. The most celebrated Whirlwind was the one that so faithfully powered Charles Lindbergh's *Spirit of St. Louis* through the long Atlantic night of May 19, 1927. Pratt & Whitney ordered the bearings for their new air-cooled radial Wasp that was introduced in 1925. Even the English came calling.

John Goldthwaite (who would become Allison's assistant chief engineer, and to whom the authors are indebted for his 1979 reflections on the company prepared for Indiana University's oral history program) recounted one of the earliest in the rewarding

transactions with Britain's Rolls-Royce of Derby—a relationship that endures today.

"They came and asked us to license them to make the bearings. They had copied ours, tried to replicate them. And they made bearings that were better looking than ours, better in every way, except they didn't work. And what it came down to was the microstructure of the bronze. The real secret of the thing was the way they were cooled. After our bearing had the metal poured into it, it was immediately quenched in water. And that caused the metal to freeze very quickly and gave us a microstructure that happened to be favorable. Rolls-Royce played square with us. We shared the process and they paid us a license fee."

From 1927 the bearings became a major portion of the firm's business, helping to sustain Allison well into the 1930s. The process was kept secret from everyone because patents were not granted until years after it went into use. The delay was caused because patent officials maintained there was nothing new in the process. They finally yielded, and proper legal protection was granted to the Gilman bearing.

The First Reduction Gears

The wartime jobs also gave Allison engineers their first opportunity to explore high speed gearing,

One key component of Gilman's steel-backed bearing was precise casting and quenching of the copper-lead (bronze) surface. Workmen pour an early pot cast during the bearing's development phase at Plant 1.

In a display prepared for the 1933 Chicago World's Fair is a pair of connecting rods with the Gilman bearing in place on the shaft end. Arrayed around the rods are other steel-backed bearings of various sizes.

A typical V-12 crankshaft, with six of its twelve connecting rods installed (because the rods are paired, only four are visible), shows the design of the forked blade at the shaft end and the quality of the overall finish. The right-hand end is fitted with roller bearings.

SMOKING

Above: At the height of the Liberty rebuilding contracts with the military in the 1920s, the south building of Plant 1 began to look more like a production facility. The Allison uprating package for the Liberty brought the engine from 450 hp to 570 hp while vastly increasing time between overhaul.

Right, center: Celebrating the delayed award of a U.S. patent for Norman Gilman's bearing that contributed so much to Allison and the aviation industry worldwide, this commemorative medal was struck in 1954.

Right: Purdue-trained engineer John Goldthwaite joined Allison in 1927 to begin a 33-year career during which he played leading roles in development of the V1710 and Allison's jets and many other projects. His 1979 transcriptions for the Indiana University Oral History Project were invaluable for this volume.
Courtesy, the Goldthwaite Family

a field in which Allison has remained preeminent for six decades. Their first application addressed an elementary fact of propeller-driven flight: aero engines generally produce power more efficiently at much higher rotational velocities than those at which propellers efficiently produce thrust. The goal was (and remains) an engine of low weight running at high speed to develop ample power linked to a propeller to run at lower speeds to deliver maximum thrust. That translated into gear reduction.

There were no such mechanisms in this country yet and many engineers believed it impossible to make gears light and strong enough to withstand airplane engine speeds. That sort of practical challenge was already a shop specialty to be met with one characteristic Allison approach: implement a sound design with unprecedented precision. Explains John Goldthwaite: "We had to run gears half again as fast as the handbooks would permit. But the limit existed because gearing was never accurate enough. When even minute irregularities in the gears came around too rapidly, they pounded each other and broke. We felt that if the gears were

While the history of this reduction-gear assembly is lost, the splintered prop, fractured case, and abraded bearing frame indicate severe impact during rotation. Even with the gears themselves damaged, however, the main assembly and bearings remained intact.

made with sufficient accuracy, those irregularities would be reduced to harmlessness. And that was true. So our gearing was based on very high precision, using the right alloy steels and giving the right heat treatment. Proud of their work, the men on the line gave us that precision."

Of several firms invited to compete under a Navy contract, Allison succeeded in adapting a British reduction gear design. Refinements included a two-speed Liberty engine with gearing and clutches, followed by several Liberties converted to single reduction. For much of the 1920s, Allison was the only company actively pursuing aircraft reduction gears and supplied them to Wright Aeronautical and to Curtiss as well as for military developmental projects.

And the Odd Job

Supplementing bearing and gear work was the manufacture of a high-speed, Roots-type blower for airplane engine manifold boost in the middle 1920s, prior to the advent of modern centrifugal turbosuperchargers. Allison's early models were used in government laboratories for high altitude research in South America, Italy, France, Germany, and Great Britain. The world altitude record was held for several years by Pratt & Whitney engines equipped with Allison Roots-type superchargers.

The firm's reputation attracted more than one inventor looking for developmental and even financial support. Among these inventors was a fellow named Lasley who provided Allison with what was probably the company's first hands-on exposure to gas turbines. In 1928 Lasley brought rough designs for an aircraft gas turbine that would drive a propeller through gearing. He handled combustion using a gas turbine adaptation then coming into use in airplane engines linked with a supercharger blower developed by General Electric. But he needed reduction gears because the turbine ran around 30,000 rpm, the propeller at 2,000.

Manufactured by Allison around a National Aeronautics Advisory Committee design, this early Roots-type supercharger was a prestigious addition to the company's product line. In more refined editions, Roots blowers are still produced by Allison Transmission for Electro-Motive and the Detroit Diesel Corporation.

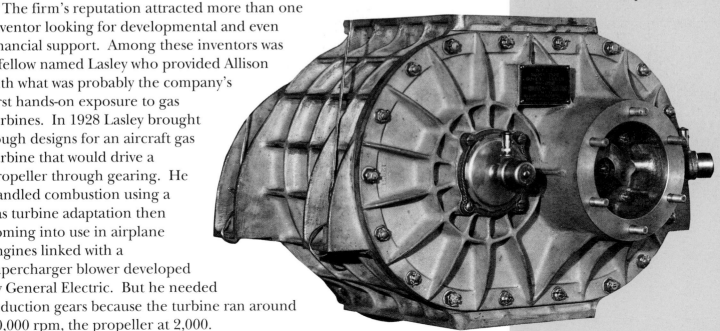

Gone is the illusion of the specialty shop in Plant 1 by the mid-1920s as the Liberty uprating and other work grew, replaced by this forest of overhead-belt-driven lathes, drills, grinders, and presses.

From Lasley's designs the Speedway crew completed the propshaft, centrifugal compressor, thrust bearings and gears, and machined the turbine and blower as a job shop, not as a financial partner. (When the turbine genie arrived again in 1944 with an unrefusable offer, the Allison welcome would be rather more receptive.) But in 1928 the Allison men knew next to nothing about gas turbines. Nor could they find anybody who knew more: others had attempted them, none had succeeded. "They were beautiful little 100-200 hp things," mused Goldthwaite about the Lasley machines forty years later, "and we made lovely gearing for him. But his combustion end never did work."

The Staff

Norman Gilman, who had run the company as vice president and chief engineer since Aitken's death in 1918, was a competent engineer who had taken an engineering course with a correspondence school, a not uncommon practice at the time and generally respected in the engineering fraternity. He had a vision for mechanical proportions and a natural aptitude for figuring things out—yet he greatly admired anyone who had mastered college mathematics.

After 1927 the staff always included at least one graduate engineer, and for some time that role fell to John Goldthwaite, whose Purdue degree in chemical engineering had covered a fair amount of metallurgy. All the engineering staff had competence in mechanical design and knew something of stress analysis. Lou Langston was

corporate secretary-treasurer and also private financial secretary to
Jim Allison, while office manager M. Wilson handled day-to-day business
details and correspondence.

One Man's Ideal

Finances varied from year to year because the shop was occupied with
so many diverse things. One project would make a small profit, another
might lose a bit. Jim Allison's only charge was, "I want the Allison name
something to be proud of." And if the shop occasionally attempted the
impossible, Allison would be pleased that they were doing things that
nobody else had the nerve or the vision to tackle. Indeed, Allison's
unique engineering company reflected his personal ideals more than it
did his ability to generate and manage wealth.

Despite his prosperity, Allison was conservative—and aware of his
investment. During one of his yearly visits to the plant to see how things
were running, he reminded Gilman and Goldthwaite, "Even a millionaire
doesn't like to lose too much money." Recalled Goldthwaite, "If we lost
some, that was all right, but the idea was we'd break even."

During the 1920s, Jim Allison's energies shifted from his Indiana
engineering and manufacturing roots to the tides of real estate
development sweeping across South Florida. His working hours were
spent planning and building in real estate-frenzied Miami, his leisure
hours on luxurious fishing yachts in the Gulf Stream. Allison's zest for
the Indiana Speedway shop was steadily fading. Perhaps the single
remaining emotion was pride. One contemporary recalled hearing
Allison speak of turning the company over to his employees.

Another Man's Vision

This almost imperceptible change affecting Allison Engineering was
apparent to Norman Gilman, who occasionally voiced his concern to
colleagues. Gilman believed the company should have a solid product
line to ensure continuity and security for the staff to whom he felt a keen

*Looking southwest, across
Main to 13th Street, c. 1923,
both buildings of Plant 1 in
Speedway are visible. Jim
Allison's office occupied the
southeast second floor corner
of the south building.*

Right and facing: These elevations of the first building of Plant 1 were prepared by the H.L. Bass Company in 1917 when the 81-foot chimney was added and modifications to the rear of the structure were made.

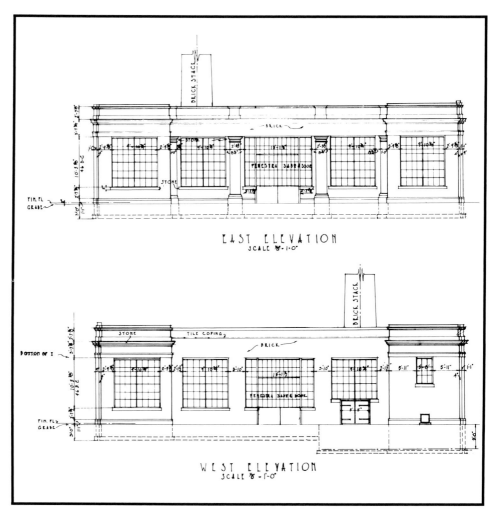

EAST ELEVATION
SCALE ⅛"-1'-0"

WEST ELEVATION
SCALE ⅛"-1'-0"

Individually-powered machines replaced the overhead belts to provide lower sound levels, better light, and greater productivity throughout Plant 1, c. 1920s.

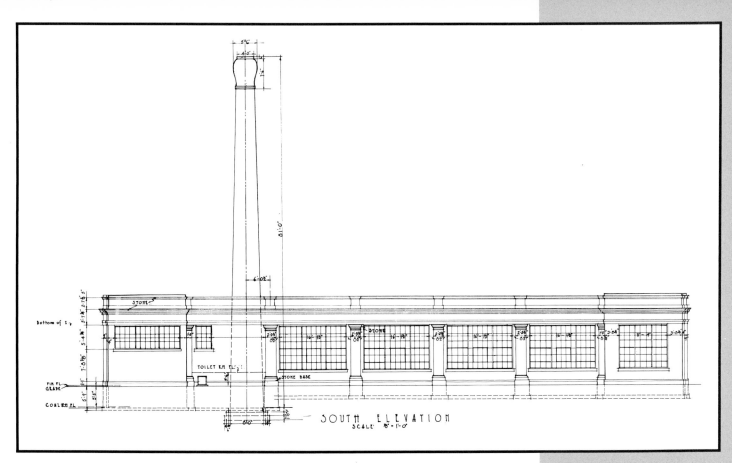

duty. The gears and bearings were a promising start, but something else was needed. As the decade waned, Gilman began to consider an idea that might just solve a whole array of problems. Airplanes were getting bigger and bigger, operational requirements ever more demanding for both civil and military aircraft. It probably wouldn't be long before designers would be looking for much more powerful engines, perhaps even as powerful as 1,000 horsepower.

The Founding Era Ends

Norman Gilman may have been pondering the challenge of product continuity in late July 1928 as he readied the Allison plant for an anticipated visit of the founder and owner. But the visit was not to be.

Beneath a banner headline, the *Indianapolis News* front page of Saturday, August 4, 1928, recited the facts:

"After an illness of only a few days, James A. Allison, widely-known Indianapolis capitalist and one of the founders of the Indianapolis motor speedway, died Friday evening at his Indianapolis estate, Riverdale, on West Riverside Drive, of bronchial pneumonia. Mr. Allison Sunday afternoon was married to his secretary, Miss Lucille Musset of Miami, at the home of Carl G. Fisher, Montauk Point, Long Island. The day following he contracted a heavy cold and on Tuesday started on a business trip to Indianapolis. He became seriously ill while on the train and on arriving here Thursday morning was taken to his home where his condition steadily grew worse. Mrs. Allison was at the bedside when the end came. Allison, fifty-five, was widely-known in the American automotive world, and through his extensive business and real estate holdings in Indianapolis and in Florida. Burial will be in Crown Hill cemetery."

As always with the death of one so vital, accomplished, and involved, personal sadness and tributes flowed to the family and the company he created. In the sorrow of the moment, tomorrow was of little interest to the public.

But for the lively enterprise Jim Allison had begun and nourished in Speedway, tomorrow could not wait. Even as probate lawyers reviewed the Allison estate, executives in Detroit were preparing to launch the Allison Engineering Company on the next leg of its journey to the future.

CHAPTER 3
Establishing

180905

Allison on the block, bidders, buyers, and plans; the Fisher brothers of Detroit. General Motors and fledgling aviation, industry contexts; GM acquires Allison. The aero engine in 1929, air- vs. liquid-cooling; Prestone. Gilman, the 1,000 hp engine; beginnings of the V1710. Army Air Corps and Navy engine ideas; airships, fighters, carriers, and politics.

Whatever the Allison Engineering Company may have been when its engineers and craftsmen headed home for supper and the weekend on Friday afternoon, August 4, 1928, Jim Allison's company was something else when they came back to work Monday morning.

For Norman Gilman and the staff, the next few months were certainly marked by anxious moments. But the work of the company continued uninterrupted while Allison executors and attorneys sorted out the estate. Because all his life Jim Allison had shared his interests, desires, and pleasures enthusiastically with close friends and colleagues, his executors knew how he felt about the company he had founded and its place in Indianapolis. That may be one reason why Allison Engineering was put up for sale with the stipulation that offers would only be considered from buyers intending to maintain its assets and operations in Indianapolis for a period of 10 years.

In any case it made good business sense that the company's worth as a going concern was greater than its value as lifeless property and equipment. Given Allison's complex and specialized operation, however, it was evident that viable interest would probably have to come from outside the Indianapolis business community.

Changing the Guard

Several prospective buyers were approached, but none were willing to accept the stipulations. Two offers came from the East—one from Wright Aeronautical, the other from Consolidated Aircraft. Wright proposed to truck away the machinery they could use and offer jobs to interested staff at their Paterson, New Jersey, base. Neither company wanted to run a plant in Indianapolis.

A third offer late in the year from a Michigan group was far more attractive. Not only were the buyers prepared to accept the estate's near-half-million dollar valuation of Allison Engineering assets, but they readily affirmed their intention to leave the firm intact and operational. Details of the sale were confirmed, and on January 1, 1929, nominal control of Allison Engineering passed to Fisher & Company of Detroit. Eddie Rickenbacker was named president.

Fisher & Company?

Neither public nor company records of those first months of 1929 reflect concern about one element of the purchase that to some must have caused alarm. There was speculation that perhaps brothers Lawrence P. and E.J. Fisher had more in mind than operating a small, specialized engineering company in Indiana. The brothers were not just owners of Fisher & Company, but also members of the executive committee of General Motors Corporation, then actively exploring opportunities for GM in the emerging aviation field. Some observers believe that in the purchase of Allison Engineering the Fishers were acting on behalf of General Motors, which would buy Allison in its own right just 90 days later.

Other facts support the Fishers' stewardship role, and an early clue may have been a visit to Gilman's office one afternoon early in March 1929. A well-dressed fellow walked in and asked to look around the shop. He introduced himself this way: "I'm Charles Wilson, vice president of General Motors, and we're thinking of buying this place."

This is the stuff of legend. The documentary evidence is less colorful. First, the eventual sale to GM was disclosed through the Marion County Probate Court, which was also assured by GM of the corporation's intention to maintain Indianapolis operations. Second, GM's March 26,

1929, appropriation request covering the Allison purchase authorizes purchase payment to Fisher & Company "at the price paid by them plus 6% interest during the time they have held *the investment* (emphasis added)." Actual authorization records show the effective purchase date as April 1, 1929. Interestingly, GM president Alfred P. Sloan, Jr., did not announce the transaction publicly until May 24. The May 25 edition of the *Indianapolis Star* reported the purchase price as $525,000, and added, "Included are the two Speedway buildings and 14 adjacent acres. Eleven additional adjoining acres were purchased on March 24." The March GM documents show some $800,000 committed to the project—$600,000 for the initial purchase plus an additional $200,000 for improvements. Allison records show earnings of some $240,000 for 1929.

General Motors and Aviation

GM's purchase of Allison was only a small element in a much larger scheme. During the 1920s the aeroplane was moving from romantic fantasy into practical utility. Not unrelated to the glamour associated with aviation as a result of the first World War and its aftermath, the 1920s generated hundreds of aviation-oriented enterprises: visionary designers, daring pilots, aerial circuses, route mappers, airport- and airplane-owning movie moguls, aeroplane and engine makers who soared one day but crash-landed the next. Hundreds of pioneering companies were formed, bought, sold, merged, reformed, and dissolved. Some thrived.

After April 1, 1929, Allison references to "the corporation" and "Detroit" would evoke the image of the 15-story building at 3044 West Grand Boulevard in downtown Detroit—the 20-million-cubic-foot General Motors Corporation headquarters building completed in November 1920.

Astute corporate observers were not long in recognizing the enormous commercial potential of aviation. Charles Lindbergh's transatlantic flight in May 1927 was high drama and made an authentic hero of "The Lone Eagle." Historians now recognize the event as a milestone that effectively legitimized aviation to the general public.

Public acceptance meant that aviation was entering the economic mainstream. For companies properly prepared, aviation's commercial promise could be fulfilled. A number of the most influential managers at General Motors, including Charles Kettering, Charles Wilson, and president Alfred Sloan, Jr., intended to see that the corporation was indeed prepared.

The Allison acquisition was only one, and the smallest at that, of General Motors' commercial aviation-related acquisitions in 1929. The larger investments exceeded $23 million and included a 24 percent interest in Bendix Aviation Corporation and 40 percent in Fokker Aircraft Corporation of America. The long-range GM view was summarized in the 1929 annual report: "GM, in forming this association with the aviation industry felt that, in view of the more or less close relationship in an engineering way between the airplane and the motor car, its operating organization, technical and otherwise, should come into contact with specific problems of transportation by air. Through this association GM will be able to evaluate the development of the industry and determine its future policies with a more definite knowledge of the facts."

Indeed, GM was to "evaluate the development of the industry" by investing at one time or another in every major aspect of aviation, including airplane and engine manufacture as well as airlines. Among the companies which GM owned outright or had a major interest in were Fokker, General Aviation, North American Aviation, Eastern Air Transport (later Eastern Airlines), Transcontinental Air Transport, and Western Air Express. Writing years later, Alfred Sloan said of the Allison purchase: "By our standards, it was a small operation: the company had fewer than 200 employees in 1929, and manufacturing facilities occupied only about 50,000 square feet of floor space. We considered it to be only of minor importance in our plans to enter the aviation industry. Yet as events turned out, we were to make Allison our principal link to the industry."

Allison's size was not imposing by GM standards, but the particulars of its work in progress were both technologically interesting and filled with commercial and military possibilities.

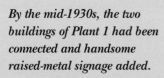

By the mid-1930s, the two buildings of Plant 1 had been connected and handsome raised-metal signage added.

Strength in Diversity

The company was a major player in the era's brief excursion into rigid airships, the zeppelins. For the Navy's *Shenandoah* in 1923 the shop designed and built reduction and reverse gearing, extension shafts, and vibration dampers. Next came an invitation from Goodyear to bid on construction of a prototype extension shaft gear drive. Said John Goldthwaite, "We agreed on condition that if it tested satisfactorily on the flexible test stand at Akron, we would build all eight devices for the ship, and spares—an attractive bit of business. They gave us a set of tentative drawings and agreed to let us build the drive system as we saw fit. It involved a very long shafting which had not been used in aircraft before. It was entirely successful at about 50 or 75 hours testing. They were very much pleased with it."

For the first engine of its own design for the military, Allison in 1924 built a 4,520-cubic-inch experimental X-type, 24-cylinder air-cooled engine that generated more than 1,200 hp. Although the Army Air Corps abandoned interest in huge single-engine airplanes before the Allison could be used, the monster motor was considered significant enough for display at Chicago's Century of Progress Exposition ten years later.

Airships and Diesels

The airship shafting job led to Allison's earliest work with diesel engines four years before GM itself began development of the type. The first Zeppelin-type airships were gasoline powered, but both the U.S. Navy and commercial operators were attracted by the long-range capabilities of the diesel engine. At the Navy's request in 1927, work was begun in Speedway on a six-cylinder, in-line engine with intake ports on the bottom, four exhaust valves, and a Roots-type blower, with

Top, left: The first engine whose basic design originated with Allison was the X4520, a 24-cylinder, air-cooled engine built in 1924 for the Army Air Corps.

Above: Viewed from inside the airship envelope, the layout of mounts, radiators, and plumbing for the German Maybach 600-hp engines and their Allison gears and shafting can be seen.

Apparent in this disassembled airship angle drive is the unit's substantial structure and precision finish, essential for smooth and reliable operation.

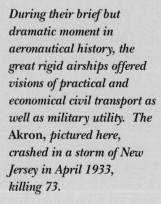

projected horsepower of about 900 and a weight of less than 3,000 lbs. By the time the engine was actually developed, the Navy's interest in lighter-than-air operations had ceased as a result of a series of fatal airship crashes.

Before their demise airships contributed another element of innovation at Speedway. The Navy's zeppelins—*Los Angeles, Akron,* and *Macon*—were powered with German Maybach engines that produced under 600 hp and weighed 2,500 lbs. Anxious to re-engine the ships with more powerful, American, engines, the Navy contracted with Allison in 1931 for a fully-reversible engine in the 650-hp class that would run at about 2,400 rpm. After several years the engine passed preliminary type qualification, and two were built for flight test installation on the *Macon*. Workers were literally bolting the shipping boxes together to ship them to Sunnyvale, California, when the *Macon* broke up in the Pacific on February 12, 1935.

Allison's development of diesel engines started four years before GM itself began research on the type. For the Navy in 1927, work was launched on a six-cylinder, 900-hp unit that weighed less than 3,000 lbs. By the time the engine was developed, the Navy had abandoned lighter-than-air operations.

Shaping a Plan

For Allison the airship episodes were a useful exercise in design innovation. But with the GM acquisition, Norman Gilman's postponed search for a product to sustain Allison began to move toward serious implementation.

At its May 14, 1929, meeting, the General Motors Operations Committee appointed a special project committee for newly-acquired Allison. Its members were Charles Wilson, Ormand Hunt, Charles F. Kettering, and Norman Gilman. Its charge: "To consider the airplane engine program and formulate a plan for the Allison Engineering Company to decide what types of engines for aviation we should build."

Well before that meeting Gilman had a detailed vision of what they ought to build: a replacement for the obsolete Liberty, a wholly modern engine that should be powerful beyond anything yet attempted.

How Much Power?

As the air transport business was beginning to grow up and the Army was beginning to re-equip after World War I, Gilman had watched the increasing speeds of airplanes and the growing need for power. Said Goldthwaite, "Each year the Army would introduce a new plane with a little more power and a little more speed, you know; they'd have a competition. Gilman plotted a curve of the annual power increases. 'Look, Johnny,' he said, "1925 is this, 1927 is this, 1930 is this, and so

During their brief but dramatic moment in aeronautical history, the great rigid airships offered visions of practical and economical civil transport as well as military utility. The Akron, pictured here, crashed in a storm of New Jersey in April 1933, killing 73.

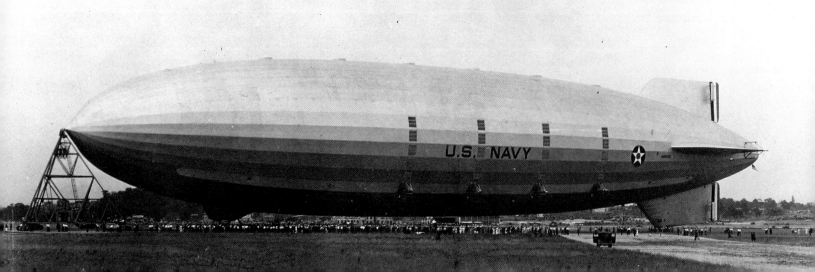

forth, and it's going up. Somebody had better start an engine aimed at 1,000 horsepower."

From the Liberty, the Allison design team had unsurpassed knowledge of water-cooled engines. Having spent years refining that one design, they knew what to avoid, particularly the difficulties of cooling and differential metal expansion. They were determined to design for high temperatures from the beginning and minimize the distortions common when aluminum and steel are present in the same structure. Next they agreed to plan for a 1,000-hp unit that would begin at a relatively conservative 750 hp, a power level they thought could be "sold" to the military.

Breaking the Water Barrier

Part of the Liberty's success lay in its cooling system. Water-cooling offered high mechanical reliability through inherently rugged construction where heat dissipation can be precisely controlled. But, reliable and powerful as it had become with Allison modernization, the water-cooled Liberty was critically design-limited. Its front-mounted radiator's huge surface area presented enormous wind resistance at higher speeds. But about 1927, someone conceived the idea of changing the coolant from water, which boils at 212° Farenheit, to Prestone (ethylene glycol) which boils at 357° Farenheit, permitting operation at proportionally higher temperatures. The higher the temperature, the smaller the radiator needs to be because high temperature is easily radiated. That allowed radiators small enough to streamline engines until their air resistance was negligible.

In an early experiment with Prestone, the Curtiss Airplane and Engine Company modified their water-cooled V-12 Conquerer. Problems with the penetrating and solvent characteristics of the coolant resulted in hot spots in the cylinders even though engineers went to 300° and a much smaller radiator.

In June 1929 Gilman hired Harold Cominez, an experienced aircraft engine designer. Early the following year he assigned Cominez as project engineer to devote full time to design of an engine to be called, from its basic configuration and the displacement capacity of its 12 cylinders in cubic inches, the V1710.

CHAPTER 4
Anticipating

*Selling the V1710 to the military.
Hazen, Detroit, and making the V1710
work. It flies. The altitude question,
supercharging and turbosupercharging;
Congress and defensive weaponry;
the P-40. The first large orders;
manufacturing on the threshold of war;
tooling up, the best of Allison meets the
best of GM. Extraordinary tasks and
men; labor, plant, process.*

Previous page: The Allison V1710 engine that would become one of history's great powerplants spent a fair portion of its first decade in this setting—roaring along on the test stand turning the dynamometer hour after hour. The precise contribution of the horseshoe went unrecorded.

Although the powerplant would appear in differing configurations to accommodate the airplanes in which it was installed —and in virtually continuous variants as power output was increased from 1936 until production ended —this F model unit typifies the Allison V1710 engine.

O n May 7, 1929, Norman Gilman and his team began to sketch the V1710 engine design, not unsurprisingly with some of the Liberty's best elements and some from the Rolls-Royce V1650. The premise was an engine of 750 hp at the outset with plenty of room for growth to 1,000 hp. But neither the Army Air Corps nor the Bureau of Aeronautics at the Navy were sufficiently convinced by Gilman's enthusiastic advocacy to commit development money. Even in Detroit the power seemed excessive. If that much power should ever be needed, they said, multiple engines would be best, not single engines. From on high came the message: aim at 800 hp.

By 1939 Gilman's power projections would be vindicated by events. But technical innovation is often impeded by short-term thinkers. Conservative military men were not persuaded by oral argument, however eloquent. They could be convinced by accumulated operational evidence, but that took time. Slowly the inevitable need for greater speed and load-carrying capacity gained momentum. Airframe makers and armed services planners began to appreciate the potential virtues of the more powerful, streamlined liquid-cooled engine concept.

The First Order

Gilman's first sale was modest. On June 26, 1930, the Navy Department's Bureau of Aeronautics contracted for design and development of the GV1710A engine rated at 750 bhp at 2,400 rpm. The prototype was delivered March 12, 1932. After three failed attempts, the engine passed its 50-hour acceptance test in September. But by then, Navy brass had committed the branch to air-cooled engines because they were shorter—then just one ring of cylinders—and easy to store on aircraft carriers. And, in a controversy made meaningless 20 years later, its detractors viewed the liquid-cooled engine as fragile prey to the first stray bullet to puncture the plumbing. So the Navy's Allison prototype and in-service Packards were shoved over the side in favor of Pratt & Whitney and Wright radial air-cooled Wasps and Cyclones.

Early Optimism

The V1710's next seven years had a touch of period Hollywood about them. In hushed drafting rooms, industrious model shops, roaring test cells, austere military offices, and even airplanes in flight, plucky engineers, devoted craftsmen, hard-headed colonels, and a corporate vice president assembled to create a plot that was accelerated by the looming specter of a world war.

Meanwhile, back at McCook Field (later Wright Field, then Wright-Patterson Air Force Base), the Army Air Corps engine people expressed cautious interest in the engine design Gilman had shown them three years earlier. They contracted for a modified model, the XV1710-1. It was acceptance tested in June 1933 at 750 bhp at 2,400 rpm. Caution turned to haste: with increased blower capacity, the engine was promptly uprated at 2,650 rpm and dynamometer tested at 1,000 bhp for 9 1/2 hours and at 90 percent power for 41 1/2 hours under favorable mounting conditions. Confidence reigned. The XV1710-3 was contracted for on March 29, 1934, and delivered to McCook for its 150-hour type test in June. On the 18th, an additional order for a similar engine, the YV1710-3, was placed, contingent on acceptance of the XV.

The 800-hp Threshold

The steep curve of optimism flattened abruptly. On the test stand, engines balked at power above about 800 hp, and runs were noisy, baffling, and short. Starting in June 1934, Gilman and the staff grappled with cracked crankcases, vibration-fatigued crankshafts, burned valves, fractured forgings, and sheared cotters. Months of seemingly endless test stand running and corrections forced Gilman to consider radical rework of the basic design. Finally, in March 1936, Gilman suspended the tests to reassess the situation. He arranged with GM engineering vice president Ormand Hunt for the support he needed from Detroit.

Ronald Hazen and Breakthrough

In the summer of 1933, a young engineer with impressive credentials had applied for a position at Allison. Gilman had hired him.

Wright Field, Ohio, would play a crucial role in Allison affairs from the day the company began business with the U.S. military. Headquarters for the Army Air Corps and later the United States Air Force equipment development, evaluation, and acquisition processes, today's Wright-Patterson Air Force Base remains one of the Gas Turbine Division's principal marketplaces and technical forums.

In 1917 the site, owned by Charles Kettering and Orville Wright, was leased by them to the U.S. Army Signal Corps, subsequently being sold to General Motors. The land was acquired by the government in 1927. Air Corps photo, October 1934.

Ronald M. Hazen had left the University of North Dakota at the outbreak of World War I, served as a master mechanic at the 7th Aviation Instruction Center in France, and was subsequently commissioned a lieutenant and pilot in the U.S. Army Air Service. In 1919 he resumed study at the University of Michigan and graduated in 1922 with a BS in mechanical engineering. After a stint at the GM Research Corporation at Dayton, Ohio, Hazen in 1923 completed his graduate work at the University of Minnesota. In 1927 he joined the Wright Aeronautical Company in New Jersey, and two years later was assistant chief engineer of Ranger Aircraft Engine, Inc., a division of Fairchild Engine and Airplane Corporation on Long Island, New York. Promoted to chief engineer, he supervised development of the Ranger 6- and 12-cylinder, air-cooled aircraft engines.

In the early 1930s General Motors Research Laboratories technicians in Detroit were working on a pair of two-cycle engines—a large flat opposed-cylinder unit for the Army, and a small radial for a $700 flivver airplane advocated by the Department of Commerce. Hazen had been invited from Allison to apply his Ranger experience to the projects, but ultimately the GM team concluded that two-cycle technology was not yet ready for either proposed application.

By 1936 the rise of fascism threatened a fragile European peace. Air power was being tested under murderous conditions in the Spanish Civil War. Even in the climate of isolationism in the United States, military preparedness was debated with increasing vigor.

At General Motors, where the Allison operation had been given division status in 1934, the engine project the corporation had been nourishing so steadily at Indianapolis moved higher on the corporate priority list. It became the subject of frequent meetings. So Gilman's inquiry to Hunt in Detroit was treated with the urgency it deserved. The necessary approvals were obtained, and soon Hazen was back in Indianapolis, this time as chief engineer, his first assignment to head up a revitalized V1710 team.

Gilman later said, "Since the very beginning of Allison Engineering I held the title of Chief Engineer, but when I decided to get Ron Hazen back to head up engineering at Allison, I felt that here was the man who should succeed me as chief engineer."

Focus on Fuel

Hazen quickly mobilized his lieutenants—John Goldthwaite, Carl Reynolds, Charlie MacDowall, Jud Buttner, Bob Heath—and set to work. He already knew precisely where they'd start. Part of the V1710 difficulty clearly lay in customer-required changes in engine configuration. From February 1935 Air Corps officials had insisted that all 10 contract engines be modified to fuel injection, necessitating complete redesign of accessory drives and housings, intake manifolding, and cylinder head ports, even though no supplier was yet building a satisfactory fuel injector. Thirty-five years later Goldthwaite reflected on those frustrating months: "It was too early to require fuel injection. Had they let us complete the engine with a carburetor, we'd have been years ahead. We should [have been] developing engines, we should have [had] engines in flight test, and we were working on this damn fuel injection, which took a lot of engineers' time, a lot of experimental time, to test in the engine."

Hazen's first big decision as chief engineer was to revert completely to conventional carburetion for the V1710. He wasted no time in lining up his allies in the anticipated battle with fuel injection partisans at Dayton. For his first meeting with the Air Corps engine people, he asked vice president Hunt to join him. There Hazen announced that, if allowed to proceed with his plans, Allison would have a qualified V1710 ready for production in a matter of months. The Air Corps people turned skeptically to Hunt: "Can we believe Mr. Hazen is speaking with any authority?" Hunt shot back, "Mr. Hazen is our chief engineer. What he says, General Motors will back up."

Hazen had thoroughly reviewed the cumulative V1710 data and confirmed his analysis with the staff: their two fundamental problems were fuel distribution and structural weakness. First, the fuel system put too much fuel in numbers one and six cylinders, and starved numbers three and five: one pair was overloaded, the corresponding pair underloaded. Overstressed during high power output, these cylinders simply failed. Second, complying with the Army's insistence on lightness, designers had left some components too light for the greater stresses imposed by higher power demand. Summarized Goldthwaite, "Light weight per unit of horsepower is essential, but you don't get it by cutting weight but by increasing power with what you have. So Hazen put extra metal where it was needed and eliminated other weak spots with improved castings."

The Type Test

Thirteen weeks later, on June 13, 1936, the first "new" YV1710-3 with redesigned intake manifolds and strengthened components was hoisted gingerly from the truck to begin its 150-hour type test. As the reassuringly steady roar in the cell passed the 140-hour mark, the Allison team in Dayton wired a cheery progress report to Gilman at Indianapolis.

But even as Gilman, who had been planning his retirement for months, asked his secretary to type a retirement letter for signing in the morning, a disqualifying crack developed on the engine's left cylinder head. A new head was installed and a penalty run begun; at 245 hours, the right head failed.

It Flies

Despite the failures, Hazen's group believed they were close to success. So did the military, who released the remaining eight contract engines for fabrication in September. Among the eight was YV1710-9, the ninth unit to be built, and the first to fly.

On a chill December afternoon, a small group of observers from Allison and the Army Air Corps watched a modified two-seat Consolidated A-11-A lift off the Wright Field runway. The flight's success had equal parts of Norman Gilman's dream, the skilled determination of Ron Hazen's able colleagues, and the character of the young company's late founder.

Said Gilman years later, "I cannot tell how we got any particular idea. You talk to one man and that starts you thinking, then someone else tells you something and that starts you off on another track. By and by your thoughts start crystallizing and finally you get a definite idea. But I do know that if it had not been for Jim Allison I would never have built that engine."

On April 23, 1937, the V1710 engine passed its 150-hour acceptance trials, America's first airplane engine to qualify at 1,000 hp. But plenty of work remained for the engine team, for airframe makers and installation engineers, and ultimately the division and the entire General Motors family.

Ironically, even though amassing 300 flight test hours on the V1710 over the Ohio and Indiana countryside, the A-11-A was essentially an antique aeroplane, ill-suited to flight test a 1,000-horsepower engine. The

Developed from a 1930 Lockheed design, 50 units of the Consolidated Aircraft P-30 were built in San Diego following the company's move there from Buffalo in 1935. Several of the ships were built as A-11s, a low-level attack fighter-bomber powered by a 675-hp Curtiss Conquerer water-cooled engine. This A-11-A served as the first testbed aircraft for the V1710.

The Curtiss XP-37, with YV1710-7 installed, was the second V1710 installation. The airframe, originally designed for a radial engine, is conspicuously hybrid, and was soon outclassed by the P-40. Capt. S.R. Harris of the Flight Test Section posed with the airplane in July 1937.

next two testbed airframes were some improvement—a Curtiss XP-37 adapted from its original air-cooled design in 1937, and Larry Bell's twin-engine XFM-1 Airacuda attack bomber of 1939. The Air Corps people were pleased enough to order 60 more V1710s; and Norman Gilman did, in fact, sign his delayed retirement letter, effective December 31, 1936.

A New Era for Allison

Anticipating the profound metamorphosis now underway for the Speedway operation, in mid-1936 Detroit had selected for Gilman's successor as general manager O.T. "Pop" Kreusser. He was a man respected for proven skills in large project management, particularly at the GM Proving Grounds and Chicago's Museum of Science and Industry. For about six months, Gilman and Kreusser worked together before Gilman retired.

At Speedway, Hazen's team suddenly faced a puzzlement carefully reported by John Goldthwaite: "You see, we built the engine to test on a mechanical and electrical dynamometer, to be bolted to the dynamometer stand, none of us dreaming that it had to be mounted later on in an airplane that didn't have a couple of horizontal steel stringers! They had to improvise ways to get that engine into a plane. Until we actually developed 1,000 horsepower with more than 100 hours testing, they never put an engine in an airplane. And when they did finally put an engine in an airplane, everybody was amazed at what it would do in the air—things nobody had ever dreamed of."

But the dreams were punctuated by plenty of tossing and turning as the new engine emerged from the relative security of the test cell to make its way in the world.

Out of the Lab and into the Sky

Early installations with Air Corps-stipulated turbosupercharging were disappointing. In March 1937 the first V1710-equipped Curtiss YP-37 performed below expectations, primarily because of high drag from the turbosupercharger and intercooler. On an early flight, the airplane was crash-landed after a supercharger fire and so was not available for the spring Air Corps Pursuit Competition. Installation of two D-type

The first multiple-engine V1710 installation came with the Bell XFM-1 Airacuda attack bomber of 1939. The pusher-type ship had expansive triple canopies, resembling the era's streamline concepts.

YP1710-9s in pusher layout for the Bell XFM-1, first flown in September 1937, encountered similar turbosupercharging drag problems.

Increasingly frustrated with problems which they were prevented by military stubbornness from eliminating, the Hazen team was eager to proceed with an altitude-rated engine with internal first stage supercharging. The Air Corps continued to resist.

Made for Each Other

Finally, in preparation for the November 1938 Pursuit Competition, Allison enlisted the support of Curtiss managers to persuade the Air Corps to fund one of the airframe builder's experimental XP-40 aircraft

General manager "Pop" Kreusser (left) and chief engineer Ron Hazen visited a test cell of an early V1710 around 1939. Under Hazen's dynamic leadership the engine matured through early growing pains into a reliable and production-ready engine.

The Curtiss Pursuit of 1939 provided the V1710 its first opportunity to prove the merits of a 1,000-hp liquid-cooled powerplant, in an Army Air Corps competition.

for mating with an altitude-rated C-type V1710 minus the external turbosupercharger. The engine was delivered in September 1938, but the competition was postponed until spring 1939.

For Allison, Curtiss, and the Air Corps, the results were surely worth waiting for as the handsome and thoroughly modern-looking XP-40 flashed through her trials at an astonishing 40 mph faster than the previous winner. The revolutionary XP-40 left the remaining competitors fairly lumbering around the course. Presumably, however, Air Corps officers present were more judicious in their enthusiasm than they had been in February with the Lockheed XP-38 prototype.

Lightning Strikes

In June 1937, responding to an Air Corps design competition for a high-altitude interceptor capable of speeds to 360 mph, Lockheed Aircraft Corporation designer Kelly Johnson and chief engineer Hall Hibbard had offered the winning Model 22. For the twin-engine, twin-boom contract prototype designated the XP-38, Lockheed chose counter-rotating C-type V1710s. The airplane made its maiden flight from March Field near Riverside, California, on January 27, 1939.

So dazzling was the silvery XP-38's initial performance that normally level-headed generals were persuaded to authorize dispatch of the lone prototype on a transcontinental speed record attempt after only five hours of flight testing.

On February 11 the XP-38 left March Field for Long Island's Mitchell Field. Pausing for fuel at Amarillo and Dayton, the Air Corps pilot sizzled along at speeds exceeding 400 mph. But, while letting down to Mitchell after an elapsed time of 7 3/4 hours, the pilot crash landed on a golf course. As a result, P-38 flight testing was delayed for many months.

The significance of the P-40 and P-38 successes was not lost on military planners in Britain and France, especially when viewed alongside parallel developments over Berlin. In April 1939 Fritz Wendel's Messerschmitt B-109 set a world's speed record of 469 mph: his engine was a liquid-cooled, in-line, 1,000-hp Daimler-Benz.

Great Britain had the excellent Rolls-Royce liquid-cooled Merlin, but its aircraft industry, unaccustomed to mass production, was hampered by lack of technicians, tools, and skilled labor. For much of the decade, the French had focused on domestic and overseas commercial air operations to the virtual exclusion of military aviation. Both realized the inadequacy of their defenses and moved to order the new U.S. airplanes and Allison engines. By May 1940 overseas orders were in hand for more than 4,000 V1710s.

Only General Motors

In Speedway and Detroit, even though management had been broadening Allison capabilities, the V1710 phenomenon was about to expand exponentially. The enormous depth and diversity of the far-flung General Motors Corporation would shortly transform its Allison Division from an engineering model shop into a production giant in a feat of unprecedented organizational ingenuity and energy.

Assistant Secretary of War Louis Johnson personally asked General Motors president William Knudsen that the corporation establish a plant for production of V1710 engines, even though the government could not then guarantee additional engine orders or fund the building.

In May 1939, a month before a contract for 969 engines was awarded by the Army Air Corps, ground was broken for the new 360,000-sq. ft. factory and office building that would be known as Plant 3. When production began there in February 1940, the Allison payroll had climbed from less than 600 the previous May to 1,702 employees. Schedules that had included perhaps 200 engines per year now projected thousands. And it was clear that experienced managers of every sort were the first priority.

Recruiting of men from the outside to fill these vital jobs was out of the question. Even had they been available, to shape an efficient team of men from different industries, accustomed to differing operations and procedures, would take far too long. But the immense worldwide GM organization with its firmly established corporate culture and diverse operations provided the answer.

While few GM people outside of Allison had ever seen an aircraft engine, they knew production. In coming to dominate the auto industry,

General Motors had refined methods and procedures which these men knew as intimately as they knew their faces in the shaving mirror. Soon highly experienced design and production engineers began arriving from all points of the compass to form the nucleus of key men around whom, with amazing speed and efficiency, an organization of more than 12,000 employees would be built by December 1941.

The "imported" executives in 1940 were as imposing as the tasks they undertook. In August, Frederick C. Kroeger, who as general manager of Delco-Remy Division was regarded as one of the best production men in General Motors, was named general manager of Allison. The new works manager was Bill Guthrie who, from his position as production head at General Motors' Opel works in Germany, caught virtually the last boat from a German port to the U.S. Under him were combined tooling, manufacturing, standards, inspection, and plant engineering. Bert Conway, general master mechanic from Pontiac, became general production superintendent; C.M. Jessup, production manager at Delco-Remy, became manager of material control; and R.C. Smith came from AC Spark Plug as chief inspector. Staff jobs in turn were filled with senior GM experts in the appropriate disciplines.

Among America's historic airplane makers, none has produced airplanes more consistently handsome or effective than Lockheed. Among the company's great successes was the 1937 Model 22/XP-38. As the P-38 Lightning, some 10,000 were built and powered with counter-rotating C- and F-type V1710s to become one of WWII's most successful warplanes.

The old timers were in their old jobs where their experience fit. And both above and below top management at Allison were more seasoned General Motors professionals: men like Robert K. "Bob" Evans, head of GM's engine group and a veteran of overseas production; Charles Kettering, the corporation's irrepressible research wizard; Ormand Hunt, the engineering vice president who had risen from the ranks through the Chevrolet mass production organization. All left their Detroit homes to take up virtual residence in Allison's Indianapolis offices where the lights seldom cooled.

Everything was orchestrated, and divisional location was no hindrance. The V1710 components were analyzed and matched against the particular strengths and resources of every GM manufacturing facility. Because of its fabled craftsmanship, for example, Cadillac took on the crankshaft, connecting rods, and reduction gears, while Delco-Remy specialized in aluminum and magnesium castings.

From Artisans to Neophytes

The immensity of the task in Speedway lay partly in the V1710 itself. It was a highly complex mechanism of some 8,000 parts that must transmit enormous stresses within precise tolerances under widely varying conditions, most of them severely punishing. A special responsibility accompanied every step in engine building: failure in service could kill a pilot.

Now, from the deft hands of the engineers and craftsmen who had created it, the V1710's destiny would pass largely into the care of earnest men and women with no previous related experience. The first machinists at Allison had come from automobile factories of Indianapolis, especially the National Motor Car Company. But now, there was no local pool of highly skilled labor.

As the agony of global warfare deepened, a transformed Allison Division was flexing its muscles in the unaccustomed role of manufacturing giant. General Motors the corporation and General Motors veterans had taken over and production began to grow. The 48 engines of 1939 became 1,153 in 1940 and 6,433 in 1941. Plenty of challenges remained, but the new team had made a gallant start. By December 7, 1941, some 6,000 V1710s were fighting in the skies over England, Africa, and China. The men and women who created those engines, however, had only begun to fulfill the limitless potential of the Allison organization.

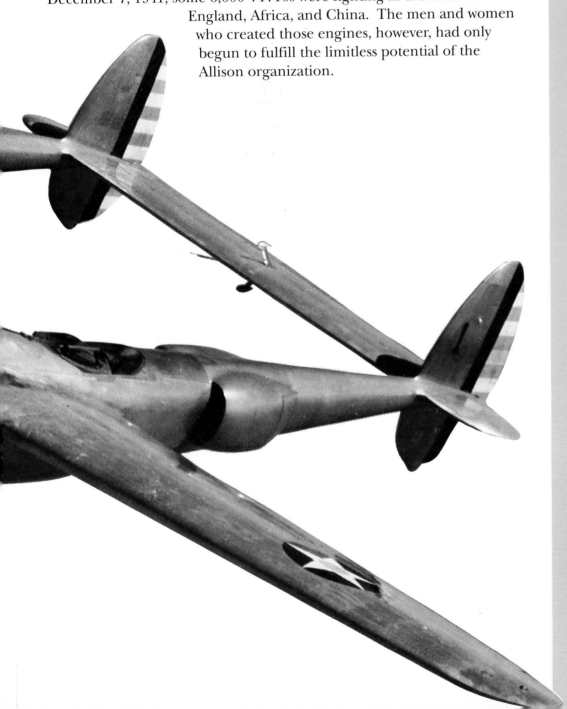

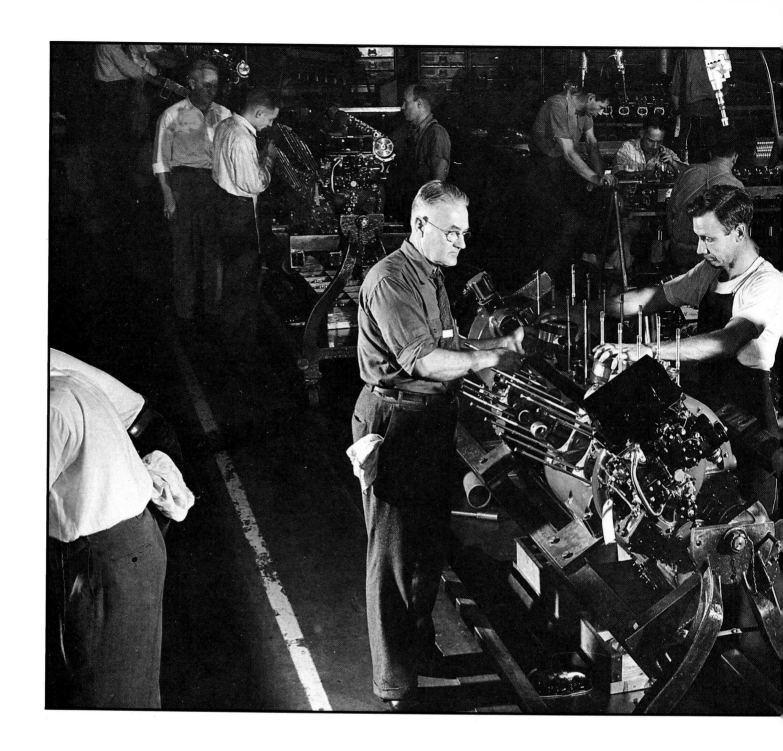

CHAPTER 5
Triumphing

*The V1710 and Allison at War.
Engine development and engineering
philosophy; job shop and assembly line.
Relations with GM divisions.
Craftsmanship, testing, special problems.
Ed Newill; GM production experts and
management people; tooling, plant
expansion. Personnel recruiting, training,
labor unions. Morale, the "E" Awards.
Tigers, Warhawks, Lightnings, Airacobras,
and Mustangs.*

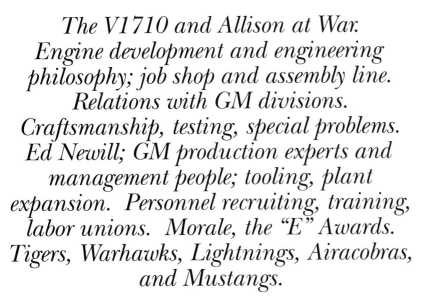

*Indisputably one of
America's most
imaginative and
effective technologists
and business leaders
was electrical
engineer, inventor,
and long-time GM
vice president
Charles Franklin
"Boss" Kettering
(1876-1958). In his
leadership role at
GM, his judgment
frequently affected
Allison's destiny.*

In its early days Jim Allison's enterprise had enjoyed the freedoms and privileges of its founder's wealth. The people who worked in Speedway shops and offices concentrated their talent and energy on elegant solutions to technical problems, largely at a pace of their choosing, largely untroubled by marketplace realities.

Since 1929 Norman Gilman's group had fared better than many small companies, in part because of their integration into the General Motors organization. But they also generated current and potential products of genuine commercial viability. During the Depression years Allison had produced at a modest profit the bearings and reduction gears that became aviation industry standards. And in the V1710 they were creating a modern aircraft engine of unprecedented power and serviceability.

In 1939 this small Midwest engineering company was swept into preparation for war. Virtually overnight the comparative calm of design, fabrication, and testing of 14 engines in a decade and the measured production of bearings—the work of 500 engineers and craftsmen in two small buildings—erupted into a tumultuous frenzy of flat-out, maximum-volume production. Although the change must have been startling for Allison's Speedway staff, company decision-makers in Detroit and Indianapolis reacted swiftly with a characteristic midwestern practicality both balanced and resolute.

The GM Commitment

Having accepted the challenge of building as many V1710s as possible as quickly as possible, General Motors and Allison managers assessed their needs, established priorities, and began implementing a plan even as they marshaled their resources—people, raw materials, plant, and systems. Concurrent with William Knudsen's agreement to build the new plant in May 1939 came the crucial commitment of the General Motors organization itself. Its pool of management skill and experience was led by Alfred Sloan, Charles Wilson, Charles Kettering, and Ormand Hunt.

The Manufacturing Priority

In preparing to set up Plant 3, for example, GM experts studied V1710 drawings plate by plate, with Allison engineers at their side, to focus on design and construction for mass manufacture. Details were examined to devise the most efficient procedures for casting, grinding, drilling, heat treating, and assembly. Designers and process engineers negotiated possible modifications to ensure or improve speed, efficiency, quality. "Why is this part like this and not another way?" "Well, it must be like this because. . ." or "It could be changed like this." Having assessed the function and tooling requirements of every piece, they chose machines, tools, and fixtures to hold them, prepared needed drawings, and sent them to toolrooms in Detroit, Pittsburgh, Cleveland, and other machinery centers across the country, to be made.

They priced drills, milling machines, grinders, lathes—the whole array of conventional and special machines. They bought them, had them delivered on a specific date, and saw them oriented properly on the production line. From the time the tooling crew began their survey until the line was up and running, less than a year had passed.

There were a few glitches in the process when some key questions were not asked, or at least not in sufficient depth. Early Cadillac connecting rods, for example, were made precisely to Allison drawings. But, it developed, some drawings specified over-generous tolerances that led to inconsistent matching during assembly. Modified specifications swiftly solved the problem; and the quality of Cadillac's Allison work is legendary in Indianapolis.

Subcontracting within the corporation was a long-established part of GM's basic policy of "decentralized responsibility with coordinated control," in which "the primary responsibility for contracting, pricing, and production rested with each individual division of the corporation, subject, of course, to GM's over-all policies."

Among other divisions and subsidiaries providing parts for the V1710 were Chevrolet, New Departure, Hyatt Bearing, Delco Products, Packard Electric, AC Spark Plug, Antioch Foundry, Harrison, and Inland. From the beginning one distinction remained unblurred: the engine's manufacturing derived from the corporation, but its conception, design, and operational aspects were wholly the province of the Allison division.

Building Factories First

The quick efficiency with which Plant 3 construction progressed was partly due to Allison's staff architect J. Lloyd Allen. Allen had been hired by Gilman in the mid-1930s when prospects for the new engine suggested that perhaps 200 units per year might be built and the division was exploring an extension of Plant 2. Allen reviewed contemporary factory design standards and conferred with Allison engineers to master facility requirements for manufacturing and testing the V1710, from space and footing needs for each type of tool and machine, to work flow, ventilation, storage, and illumination.

Building the two-million-square-foot Plant 5 in Maywood in 1942 took barely four months. Construction time and scarce steel were saved with prefabricated components such as these pillars, called "thunderbirds."

Two electrical companies had displayed fluorescent lighting at the 1939 New York World's Fair, projecting commercial introduction in perhaps two years. Allison managers persuaded the companies to advance their production, and 20,000 five-foot-long tubes were delivered in 1940, the first large installation of the cool and efficient lighting type.

The Plant 3 exercise was only the first of several that would accommodate 1943's peak employment of 23,019 people and production of more than 3,000 engines per month. Building expansion continued practically without interruption.

In 1942 ground was broken for the two-million-square-foot production facility, Plant 5 in Maywood. Because of the critical steel shortage, ingenious devices such as gigantic wooden pillars called "thunderbirds" were used. From the laying of the foundation to occupancy took only three months and 27 days. In that time a factory was built that covered an area equal to 20 city blocks. The plant was visible evidence of an Allison legend that a new factory was in use before the architect's drawings were completed.

Building a New Team

Pop Kreusser had ably supervised Allison's initial expansion of manufacturing capability, drawing upon his leadership and organizational experience. However, as the enormity of Allison's 1940 production buildup was evidenced, he was among the first to recognize Allison's acute need for an expert in high volume production, and with zest he took on a new assignment as director of training and service.

When 50-year-old Frederick Kroeger arrived from Delco-Remy in August 1940, the wisdom of choosing a general manager with the strongest possible background in high volume work was proven. A 1911 electrical engineering graduate of Purdue, Kroeger had begun his career at General Electric, then moved to Remy Electric Company at Anderson, Indiana, before serving in World War I as head of electrical equipment design for the Army Motor Transport Corps. After his Army tour, Kroeger rejoined Remy, which became part of General Motors in 1918. He was made chief engineer in 1921. Elected to a GM vice presidency in December 1940, Kroeger masterfully directed the teeming complexities of Allison's mushrooming war-driven buildup.

Recruiting and Qualifying

Perhaps the greatest initial challenge facing the new Allison was to recruit, qualify, select, and train thousands of new workers. They would be called upon to perform the demanding tasks of manufacturing elaborate, precision aircraft engines in previously unimagined quantities. To meet Plant 3's initial employee complement of 3,500 and an ultimate work force of more than 20,000, the personnel department (headed from 1939 through 1944 in sequence by R. Kremer, J. Brophy, K.H. Hoffman) was soon hiring 100 people each day from all walks of life—interviewing, checking backgrounds, arranging health examinations, setting up personnel records.

Matching Men and Machines

More than half of the new employees, whose average age was 22, came from nearby Indiana communities, and from Ohio and Illinois. Because the area had no particular tradition of mechanical technology, there were precious few skilled machinists in the labor pool. The solution had two parts: first, intelligent and responsible candidates willing to learn; and second, manufacturing processes that could be accomplished satisfactorily after a relatively short training period. An overwhelming

majority of the men and women who flowed into the Speedway and Maywood employment offices proved themselves more than worthy of the Allison challenge.

The machine toolmakers were up to their challenge as well. By 1940 it had become possible to perform many precision manufacturing operations with machines that were run not by machinists but by operators: the essential skill and precision could be built into the machine and its fixtures, a method already partly developed in the automobile industry.

The thread grinder and the contour projector illustrate the process that made possible not only the manufacture of 21,381 V1710s in a single year, but indeed the entire nation's stunning industrial outpouring of World War II. Precision threading was essential to the V1710. Formerly it took a master machinist several days to set up and produce a precision ground thread on a bolt. Now the Excello Company in Detroit had designed a machine to do it automatically.

"We thought when we bought the first one that we'd need to have the most skilled grinder in the shop to run it because it was a delicate operation," said Goldthwaite. "But Excello said we didn't need an experienced grinder. So we got a boy whose total shop

After initial assembly, each V1710 was run in on the test stand and its performance measured against standard before being torn down, cleaned, and inspected prior to final assembly and shipment. In the foreground a single engine's sub-components, including the block and protruding headbolts, are laid out for assembly. To the left are banks of pistons (two banks required for each engine).

During the wartime emergency, America's factories needed many more workers than the traditional male labor pool could supply. Thousands of women nationwide answered the call for help and proved immensely able in wide-ranging assignments. Allison plants employed large numbers of women —31 percent of the work force in 1943, most of them new to the workplace. Here an inspector verifies dimensions on a gear-checking machine, c. 1943.

experience was in the barn doing minor repairs on his father's tractor, and we put him on that thread grinder. The manufacturer's representative instructed him, and within a couple of days he was doing more accurate work in making screw threads than any of our skilled machinists had ever imagined.

"The final measurement of the screw thread was made with a contour projector—like a slide projector but with a bolt in it instead of the slide—that projects a shadowgraph of the bolt with its screw threads magnified, say a hundred times, on the screen. There had been a few expensive contour projectors made before, but not for the kid on the thread grinder. Now there was a small projector with proper centers to mount a bolt on and a screen about six inches square."

Ultimately banks of thread grinders and counterpart machines for other processes were run by operators without previous skill but who were carefully selected and instructed. They were wide-awake young people eager to learn and to do good work. All they had to do was press buttons and work levers. Simple inspection devices were located beside each machine so that the operator could inspect the pieces as they were processed.

Training and Service

After Kroeger's arrival, Pop Kreusser assumed the enormous task of training Allison's burgeoning work force as well as the military and civilian personnel who would be maintaining engines in the field. Kreusser's front line "faculty" were 400 senior Allison craftsmen who introduced new employees to the world of precision machines, acquainting them with tools, processes, procedures—and the Allison universe.

A formal Training Department for V1710 service and maintenance was launched in July 1940, with two instructors and six students. By December 1943 the section had grown to 88 instructors and staff, with 11 zone offices worldwide. Facilities were leased from the Hercules Paper Box Company at Lafayette Boulevard and Holt Road from 1941 to 1945, and known as Plant 6. In addition to instruction, the unit included a

Building engines was only part of the job assumed in Indianapolis. The complex machines shipped from Allison's plants had to be properly operated and faultlessly maintained to perform satisfactorily. Training for pilots, engineers, maintenance staff, and other support people was a high-priority task from 1939 on. Service School manager Connie Martin reviews V1710 operating systems with a class of flying officers.

publications staff of 40 under Dick Tripplehorn, responsible for publishing operation and maintenance bulletins, parts catalogues, and manuals. Technical writers adapted material so it could be easily understood by both inexperienced draftees and longtime mechanics.

New Problems, New Solutions

Many of Allison's challenges arose at the frontiers of technology, in areas largely untrodden by any manufacturing organization. Early in the war Allison found existing sources inadequate to supply the intricate aluminum castings required to carry the V1710's high stresses.

At Antioch College near Dayton, Ohio, a professor and his wife had perfected the lost-wax method of casting art objects to exceedingly close dimensions in their small foundry. GM bought the foundry and hired the couple to work on applying their technique to high-strength aluminum parts. Their innovative work complemented two foundries set up at Anderson and Bedford under Delco-Remy to supply aluminum castings for Allison engines. These castings proved to be infinitely better than others available anywhere in the world—and at less than half the cost. At war's end Delco-Remy converted the Anderson foundry for its own needs and Allison purchased the Bedford Foundry. General Motors sold the Antioch shop back to the professor and his wife and paid them royalties on GM castings made with their process.

Shared Discoveries

Aviation has long been known for its sharing of technology, particularly in matters of safety. The common cause of patriotism further nourished the tradition among American aviation manufacturers. Membership in groups such as the Automotive Council for War Production, which met at plants around the country, allowed engineers to share ideas that could be carried back to their own plants.

At the Wright Aircraft Engine factory in Lockland, Ohio, near Cincinnati, for example, Allison engineers observed one of the industry's first automated systems for cylinder head manufacture. Wright had developed a continuous, fifty-foot-long automatic line to drill, bore, turn, tap, and thread the complex form of the air-cooled cylinder head. On a conveyor at one end of the line would start a casting or forging and at the first machine it would be clamped down in position for some operation. That machine would finish and the piece would be released to the next machine. After each process, a head with gauging equipment would

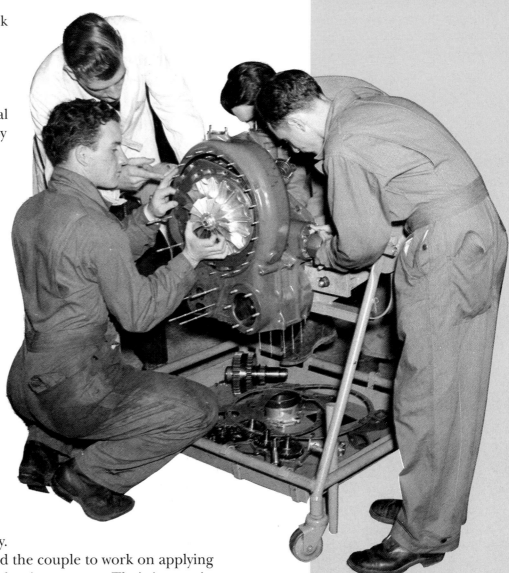

An instructor takes a new group of student mechanics through the intricacies of a V1710-E11's auxiliary stage supercharger assembly as a demonstration unit's impeller is fitted into its housing, c. 1943.

verify that the operation had been done correctly. The line required no operators, just a few men of inspector-level always watching to see that everything ran properly. Today, of course, most volume manufacturing is done that way.

Not by Machines Alone

Automated production by its nature tends to de-emphasize individuals' contributions to the finished product. Allison's necessary adoption of the process was no exception. Yet over time, memories of remarkable people endure among colleagues and in corporate records of every sort. One such engineer was Arthur W. Gaubatz, a University of Michigan-trained engineer who came to Allison in 1939 from Buick where he had been chief designer of their very successful straight-eight engine.

The V1710 at that stage was stubbornly defying efforts to correct fuel problems. Gaubatz devised a fuel control mechanism that solved the immediate difficulty and led to three separate patents. "On loan" from Buick, Gaubatz stayed with Allison until retirement in 1964, compiling 66 active, quality patents ranging from bearings to rocket motor controls.

Testing Keeps Pace

Among the most important aspects of aviation-related manufacture is comprehensive testing—because the consequences of in-service failure are unacceptable. As the V1710 was uprated in power output and adapted to various aircraft installations, new test procedures of every sort were devised. During a rash of connecting rod failures, engineer Goldthwaite devised a method of simulating engine loads on test rods at high speeds so the parts could be observed directly under load. Reported Goldthwaite: "So we built my little machine that pushed and pulled the rod with forces comparable to the engine's 20,000 lbs. Anybody would have thought that a connecting rod was just rigid, but you could actually see the thing shorten and stretch. When that's happening at speed, it just looks like rubber. And pretty soon it would break, always in the same place. Knowing the failure origin, we added about half an ounce of metal at the weak point and never lost another connecting rod to that cause."

Multiple V1710s

Responsible for coordinating the V1710's literally continuous model changes and modifications throughout its life was chief design engineer Charlie McDowall. The original C engine, the first big production model, had a fixed reduction gear ratio of two-to-one in a very long nose as originally requested by the Army for the P-40. New aircraft designs specifying different gear ratios and other changes required new V1710 models. Both the E model for the Bell P-39 and the F engine for the P-38 were designed and introduced without interrupting production, in itself a remarkable achievement. During one period, the average time between model changes on the line was just 40 days.

Simplification

Among other changes made to enhance manufacturing efficiency was the consolidation of sub-assemblies, a process which allowed the V1710's 7,000 individual parts to be reduced to 700 piece parts— separate production elements—compared to 2,300 piece parts for the Rolls-Royce Merlin. By way of illustration, parts in one sub-assembly were reduced from 38 to three by simply casting the part whole instead of building up bolted components. (Engine parts counts, it should be noted, vary by the counter and what's counted: with every nut, washer,

gasket, and cotter pin included, a random V1710 unit might run to more than 8,000 parts.)

The Life-Dependency Standard

Among the people who worked in the design rooms and on the production floor at Allison, noted one engineer, "there was a universal conviction that men were going to fly these engines, and if anything was wrong with them it would kill the pilot. We repeated that and believed it and acted on it. There were some scares where something did go wrong, where some defective part apparently passed. But when any suspicion arose that something might have been wrong, the first step was to shut down the shipping room until the problem was isolated and corrected."

Subsidiary Issues

Typical of the diverse problems that surfaced as production mounted was noise. Noise problems, both for the production and testing staff and for the community around the plants, had begun when rebuilt Liberties were tested on an outdoor stand with simple wooden walls and roof to keep the weather off the operator. Speedway City wasn't big then and complaints were often ignored. "You had to test the engines and they made noise and that was that." But testing at wartime production levels meant serious noise. The architecture and engineering books of the 1930s contained little noise data, most of it worse than useless. Pursuing their own original research and evaluation, Allison staffers pioneered noise reduction techniques, from environmental sound level assessment to anechoic baffling. Among Allison innovations were effective isolation of the test engine operator from the engine using compact electrical engine controls and sound-baffled chambers that drastically reduced noise output.

Noise in the Ear of the Beholder

In the course of their research, engineers supplemented technical discoveries with helpful people observations. Said John Goldthwaite: "Without going into the details of decibel meters, it turns out that noise is sound you don't like. If you do like it, it isn't noise; or if you are accustomed to it and choose to ignore it, it isn't noise."

In surveying the Speedway neighborhoods around Plant 3, Goldthwaite measured test engine sound levels at varying distances up to 10 miles away. "I stopped at a little grocery store to find out what people thought, and asked the woman behind the counter, 'What's that noise going on?' She said, 'What noise?' I said, 'That noise up there.' 'Oh,' she said, 'that's something about the engines up at Allison.' 'Well, doesn't it drive you crazy?' 'Oh, no,' she said, 'whenever I hear that noise I know the boys have jobs and my trade will be good.' Nearby, on the other hand, a woman was threatening to sue. Her glassware was falling off the table, and it was driving her nuts and she was going to sue us because of that noise. Two women living in houses practically side by side. One found the noise a good sign, the other headed for court."

A V1710 is torn down for inspection after its initial run on the test stand, c. 1941. Visible on the left cylinder head are the rocker arms and valve springs for the valves which control the flow of fuel vapor and exhaust gases to and from the cylinders below.

A Matter of Costs

The price of the V1710 engine was at first "pretty much guessed." The 1932 prototype was almost arbitrarily priced at $75,000, and estimates of incurred development deficits from 1929 until the engine entered production range from $800,000 to more than $1 million. The contract unit price dropped to an historic low of $9,304 in 1945.

With no relevant experience at the outset of wartime production, cost estimates were crude. Managers executed military contracts on the understanding that when the company established cost records, the contract would be renegotiated and a new price set based on actual experience. Allison managers proudly noted that all the wartime renegotiations were initiated by the company. As performance

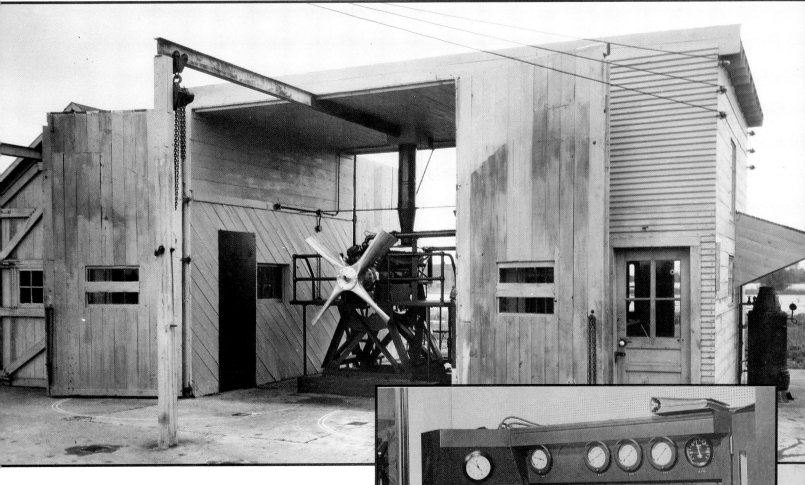

improved, lowered costs were passed along in a lower price. The military initially opposed the renegotiations but soon recognized the consistent fairness of Allison pricing.

The V3420 Goes to Sea

While V1710s were destined to earn fame and glory in every theater of the war, an attempt to launch a naval career for its big twin brother, the V3420, resulted in less success—but plenty of entertainment. Responding to the threat posed in the Mediterranean by speedy Italian naval motor torpedo boats, the British designed a boat of their own—the Scott-Payne patrol torpedo (PT) boat. In 1939 the PT boat came to the attention of President Franklin Roosevelt, a notorious enthusiast of things naval. Soon several million dollars were allocated to develop a comparable vessel for the U.S. Navy. The Scott-Payne boat with its three Rolls-Royce Merlin engines was brought to New London, Connecticut, for demonstration.

With an eye on the 2,000-hp V3420 engine, the Navy invited Allison observers to see the British boat perform. Pop Kreusser and John Goldthwaite headed east. Well out to sea the British commander opened up the throttles and the PT boat roared and hissed along at an exhilarating 40-plus knots. The Electric Boat Company was contracted to build a U.S. prototype, the PT-8. Thinking that this might be a way to get its big engine into production, Allison agreed to participate, but with reservations. Goldthwaite was put in charge of Allison's part in the project.

The planned compromise was that Allison would supply two forward-only V3420s with connect-disconnect jaw clutches. The Navy would install a 600-hp marine engine for maneuvering and reversing because the big

Top: By contrast with 1943's comparatively comfortable engine test environment, this 1925 view of the Allison 24-cylinder, X-type 4520 engine shows the simplicity of an early test stand.

Among refinements developed during WWII were vastly improved powerplant engine test cells that included control and monitoring stations isolated from the running engine. An operator logs data from a V1710 in 1943.

The biggest of Allison's wartime engines was the mighty 2,000-hp V3420 that saw limited service in such test aircraft as the XB-19 and the XB-39, and a fighter that came too late for active service, the Fisher P-75.

Two V3420s found a brief, colorful career in this prototype patrol torpedo (PT) boat, the PT-8, built by Connecticut's Electric Boat Company in 1940. Production model PTs were engined with smaller, Packard-built Rolls-Royce Merlins. The whaleback hull design, intended to shed water quickly, originated in the Great Lakes ore boats of 1888.

engines were not designed to operate at slow speeds. Said Goldthwaite: "An airplane engine performs best in every way at high speed, and it doesn't idle very well. But you have to be able to back a boat up. And we refused to design a reverse gear for a single order, but agreed that for a production order we would design a proper marine modification that would do everything."

Unplanned compromises followed, reducing the aluminum-hulled PT-8 and her trials to a comedy of errors. The engines arrived at the Philadelphia Navy Yard and were installed. Next came the twin 30-foot prop shafts, specified by Allison as steel bored out with a quarter-inch wall, to weigh perhaps two hundred pounds. The Navy, to avoid the expense of the boring, installed solid shafts that weighed three tons.

"Then," said Goldthwaite, "they decided to send that thing from Philadelphia up to the Brooklyn Navy Yard in convoy with several wooden-hulled PT boats that were unable to withstand high speeds in rough open ocean. The PT-8, on the other hand, could go either very slow with her marine engine or very fast with her Allisons, and her metal hull was untroubled by the heavy seas. All the way to Brooklyn the wooden boats forged ahead as fast as they dared go without opening their planks until almost out of sight, then the PT-8 would open up and overtake them in a wild rush, to slow down again until the wooden boats caught up. That was the whole trip to Brooklyn, and that was the end of the PT-8."

A Change in Leadership

In April 1943 general manager Fred Kroeger began a leave of absence because of poor health that would culminate in his death 13 months later. From May through July, the general manager position was held by

Cy Osborn, who would later head GM's Electro-Motive Division in La Grange, Illinois.

Ed Newill Takes Charge

On August 2, 1943, Edward B. Newill was named general manager of the Allison Division (he would be elected a GM vice president in July 1948), beginning a 17-year Allison career during which he would lead the company through some of its most challenging and productive times.

Following graduation from the Georgia Institute of Technology in 1915 with degrees in electrical and mechanical engineering, Newill began work with Westinghouse Electric and Manufacturing Company in East Pittsburgh, Pennsylvania. In 1929 he joined GM to head the General Motors Radio Corporation. The following year he was named chief engineer and director of research for Frigidaire Division, becoming division assistant general manager in 1937. In 1941 Newill became assistant to the GM group executive in charge of the household appliance and aviation divisions. In 1942, with the formation of Eastern Aircraft Division, he was made assistant to the group executive in charge of Eastern Aircraft and GM divisions in Dayton.

Ed Newill had already earned a reputation within the corporation as a problem-solver, a leader who got things done. In approaching Allison's

During a summer 1945 visit to Maywood, P-38 pilot Richard I. Bong was "interviewed" by Allison general manager Ed Newill. Medal of Honor-winner Bong recorded 40 victories over Japanese aircraft in his Lockheed Lightning to become America's greatest air ace. Dick Bong was killed in a takeoff accident in a P-80 just weeks after this photo was taken.

The Air Corps' first technical representative assigned to Allison's flight test operations, Major Jimmy Doolittle was a favorite of company engineers and support staff. His "personal" P-40, in which he commuted to and from Allison on other assignments, was often used as a test plane. In 1943, the year after his famed Tokyo raid from the decks of the **Hornet,** *Doolittle made a bond drive visit to Allison and was hosted by general manager Fred Kroeger, left.*

subsequent corporate turning points, Newill would exhibit both imaginative flexibility and cautious conservatism. In 1943 he took charge of Allison's destiny with vigorous competence and a gracious charm recalled warmly by colleagues decades later.

Among corporate accomplishments Newill recalled with pride was the Frigidaire Division's production success in making the .50 calibre machine guns which Browning and Colt designers had loudly asserted could not be mass-produced. Not only were the weapons produced in huge volume and on schedule, but were much praised by battle-tested soldiers: "A GM gun always worked."

At Allison, Newill-led achievements included the inauguration of the massive manufacturing facility at Plant 5; the flight test facilities of Plant 10 at Weir Cook Airport; the research facilities of Plant 8; the transition from piston to jet engines following World War II; and the initial work with Allison turboprops that resulted in their preeminence in military aviation.

Edward and Zilpha Newill's three sons all went to work for the corporation—Edward J., with Delco-Remy; William J. with Delco Products, and Robert B. with Pontiac Motor Division. Grandson David B. continues the 60-year Newill tradition with the Allison Gas Turbine Division.

The UAW Comes to Indianapolis

Although the United Auto Workers (UAW) during the late 1930s had managed to organize practically all the General Motors divisions across the United States, Allison's first labor union agreement appears to be a September 17, 1940, pact not with the UAW, but with the United Aircraft Engine Workers, Inc., an independent union certified by the National Labor Relations Board (NLRB).

The earliest UAW Allison-related activity is a September 17, 1941, meeting called by UAW-CIO International representative John Bartee to obtain names of 20 members to go on a charter for Allison employees. On October 12, 1941, temporary officers were elected, among them president Merritt Allen. Early in 1943 the UAW made its first effort to organize Allison workers, obtaining enough signatures for an NLRB election in April. That organizing effort was unsuccessful.

In March 1944 election of the local's first permanent officers included president Paul Eberts and vice president Arthur Skibbe. That year an office was opened in the Knights of Pythias building on North Pennsylvania Street under field representative Anthony Probe. The Local began publication of *The Rocket,* edited by F.J. Dalton of the International staff.

A second UAW representation drive resulted in an NLRB election on September 7, 1944. The UAW-CIO received sufficient votes to be declared the bargaining unit for the company. On November 22, 1944, the NLRB granted Local 933 full bargaining rights in Allison plants. Allison may have been the last of the General Motors' divisions to be organized by the United Auto workers, in part because the old-time machinists long resisted the idea that any organization outside the company itself might influence their professional affairs.

The Allison Spirit

Like much of the sentiment of America in WWII, from the perspective of half a century later a sense of the patriotism, community pride, and company loyalty that pervaded the Allison organization throughout the Second World War is not recaptured easily. Bond drives, plant visits by movie stars and military heroes, the winning of the Army-Navy "E" award, flyovers of fighters at employee picnics, and ceremonies to mark production milestones may seem quaint to a post-Vietnam generation. Nonetheless the cause was noble, its values enduring, and the accomplishment heroic.

More than nostalgia moves Allisonians to recall those homefront rituals. Dorothy Lamour, petite and glamorous with her entourage winding its way among the big machines on the shop floor and talking with workers. Bob Hope and Jerry Colonna ad-libbing to a delighted lunchtime audience. A sunny spring day rally in 1941 on Plant 3's spacious lawn, dignitaries speaking, a band playing. Then low thunder and a howling roar as a lone P-38 Lightning—flown by Allison test pilot Pinky Grimes—passes low,

In March 1944 Allison produced the 50,000th V1710. To mark the occasion, the milestone engine was "exchanged" for the first V1710 to have flown, "Old No. 9" of 1936. General manager Ed Newill joined with Maj. Gen. John Curry in an informal ceremony to mark the occasion.

Of America's movie stars during the Second World War, Dorothy Lamour was among the most generous in devoting her time to entertaining troops and headlining bond drive rallies.

The most visible symbol of the Army-Navy "E" award was the huge blue burgee to be flown from an honored company's flagpole. The 1944 banner is raised.

The company's wartime performance was, by every standard, phenomenal. General manager Fred Kroeger accepts the first of Allison's four "E" awards in 1943. Among distinguished Allison leaders at the ceremony were retired general manager and chief engineer Norman Gilman (front row, second from left) and works manager Bill Guthrie (second row, left).

climbs straight up to disappear in the blue sky above upturned faces. The genial informality of Colonel Jimmy Doolittle conversing casually with workers and secretaries. The deeply moving lobby display of a bullet-riddled V1710 engine returned home after bringing its pilot and plane safely back to base. The ceremony in March 1944 at which Ed Newill presented Army Air Force officers with the 50,000th V1710, and received in exchange "Old No. 9," the first V1710 to fly.

The "E" Award

In 1906 the United States Navy inaugurated a tradition of awarding an "E" for excellence to units that displayed exceptional loyalty, devotion, and service. After Pearl Harbor came the realization that the men and women of American industry were genuine partners with the fighting forces. So emerged the Army-Navy Production Award, a joint recognition by the Army and the Navy of exceptional performance and patriotism on the home front. Selection of recipients was made by the Boards for Production Awards and included the privilege of flying an Army-Navy "E" burgee above the plant for six months. Each employee received a silver "E" insignia pin.

Every six months following, production performance was reviewed to determine continuation of the honor. Service stars could be added to the burgee to acknowledge each half-year of continuing merit. Allison's first award came in October 1942, the second and third in 1944, and the fourth on April 21, 1945.

Continued on page 81

The V1710 at War

The Curtiss P-40—Warhawk, Tomahawk, and Kittyhawk

The P-40 and the V1710 were originally matched to accomplish a specific mission that fortunately never materialized: defensive war in North America. Strategists planning for such a contingency envisioned the U.S. having only one chance to repel invasion at unknown points along the eastern seaboard. That meant defensive pursuit planes rugged enough to survive in combat stationed at inland bases. The planes could be launched quickly with ammunition for low-level strafing and bombing and fuel to fly 700 miles or more.

After the XP-40's lively show at the delayed 1938 Pursuit Competition, the airplane served in every theatre of World War II, creating legends as she flew. From 1938 to 1944, the Curtiss-Wright Corporation built 17,738 P-40s in six principal variants for the air forces of the U.S., Britain, the Soviet Union, the Free French, and China's American Volunteer Group (AVG).

Among P-40 legends, none endures more vividly than U.S. Air Corps Major Claire Lee Chennault's AVG, the Flying Tigers, not least because of 150 or so V1710 engines unique among the 70,000 made. The AVG was formed in 1941 and comprised three squadrons trained in Burma under Chennault. One squadron went into action in China against the invading Japanese in December 1941, the others remained in Burma to reinforce the Royal Air Force.

The first Flying Tiger success came on December 20, 1941, when the group shot down six Mitsubishi bombers. Over all, the group recorded 286 confirmed victories with 12 pilots lost in action. Squadron Leader Robert

Claire Chennault's American Volunteer Group was created at the request of the Chinese government to help China defend herself from Japan. The AVG included the 3rd Pursuit Squadron—the "Hell's Angels"—stationed at Toungoo, Burma. The group's 72 pilots and ground personnel, c. 1941, were assigned 31 P-40s. Squadron Leader A.E. Olson stands sixth from left.

Far from headquarters, field maintenance is performed on a Curtiss P-40 early in WWII. Headlamps for lighting and 55-gallon drums for ladders were routine, but the hammer on the air intake probably wasn't. The Royal Australian Air Force truck and the aircraft's paint scheme suggest the South Pacific.

H. Neale scored 16 victories, Lt. Col. Gregory "Pappy" Boyington earned six and later accumulated 22 more to become the USMC's leading ace. The Tigers in 1942 were "regularized" as the USAAF 23rd Fighter Group.

The Matter of Interchangeability

In changing from Allison's original job shop system, in which each engine was built up one at a time, to the high volume production begun in 1939, component interchangeability became an important factor, from drawings to final assembly. Interchangeability was an inspection standard for the Army Air Corps inspectors assigned to accept engines for the government. Components were rejected for the most minute variation from dimensional standard.

During early production of C-model engines destined for British and American P-40s, the accumulated store of these rejected parts became the Flying Tigers' roar. When representatives of the Chinese government came to Indianapolis in late 1939 to order engines for their newly-purchased P-40s, Allison regretfully explained that every engine on the line was spoken for—by the British, the French, the U.S. Army Air Corps.

Then someone thought about the storeroom full of off-size parts. They weren't strictly interchangeable, but they were perfectly sound. Perhaps if they were matched and mated, they'd make up enough engines to meet the AVG order. The Chinese were delighted. Steel inserts were plated to fit oversize tapped holes, connecting rod bearings were altered to fit slightly undersize crankshafts, and dozens of other similar fixes were made. Some 150 engines were all hand-fitted by Allison people who had previously been engine builders for Duesenberg, Stutz, and Marmon. When tested, these units developed more horsepower and used less fuel than the regular engines which the U.S. military would accept.

"We loved to tell the story afterwards," said a retired engineer, "that in the field those engines made out of matched parts that had been rejected on Army standards had a better field record than the standard engines. We just loved to tell people that, and it was true."

Company Support for the AVG

Training director Pop Kreusser selected Tye M. Lett, Jr. and Arne Butteberg to direct the setup of maintenance operations for the AVG's engines in the field, and Chennault's crew chiefs and 11 Chinese-Americans with aeronautical experience spent up to six weeks training at Allison in Speedway. Lett and Butteberg left Indianapolis on May 12, 1941, and took Pan American's *California Clipper* on her maiden flight from San Francisco to Manila, then a Dutch steamer to Hong Kong. From there, a Chinese National Aeronautical Corporation DC-3 flew them to Burma via Chungking and Kunming.

Three Very Special Warhawks

During almost three decades at Allison, engineer Bill Thomas contributed to nearly all its engine programs, including the J71, T56, and TF41. His first Allison engine was the V1710 in the P-40, and he recalls their meeting vividly.

"In January 1939, after finishing two years of engineering at Rose-Hulman Institute, I joined the U.S. Army Air Corps to avoid being drafted into the Infantry. And I really loved airplanes. I was at Clark Field in the Philippines with the first B-17 squadron to ferry planes from Boeing Field across the Pacific.

"During the few months we fought in the Philippines, we lost our B-17s. In late December 1941 I moved 600 miles south to Delmonte on the Island of Mindanao. Twenty Air Corps engineering people, me included, were sent to the beach at a village named Bugo for different duty than we were used to.

"In early March 1942, the freighter *Western Farmer,* with a completely volunteer crew, arrived from Australia with three brand-new P-40 fighters lashed to the deck—the only Air Corps reinforcements to reach the Philippines before the fall of the islands. To prevent attack by Japanese aircraft, the ship was beached and the cargo brought ashore by a makeshift breeches buoy. Each airplane was packed in two large crates, one the fuselage with engine installed, the other the wing assembly. They were unloaded into a large coconut grove that stretched along the beach for several miles.

"We were to assemble these aircraft and to attempt to get them back to Delmonte—with few tools and no cranes or hoists. To raise the fuselage and engine components high enough to get the wing underneath and lower the gear, we commandeered a local lumber company's block-and-tackle rig that we slung in a coconut tree. Our experience was limited to air-cooled radial Wright and P&W engines. Our entire understanding of these in-line liquid-cooled engines was a study of the manuals, which luckily were included in the crates.

In the Philippines sometime in 1942, field assembly of P-40s was accomplished under somewhat more luxurious conditions than Bill Thomas found. The fuselage, with engine installed, is hoisted over the wing unit with the overhead pulley and lowered into place.

"The Allison link here is first that the manuals must have been well written indeed for a bunch of kids to understand and use successfully. Second, all three of these Allison V1710 engines had been manufactured in Indianapolis in mid-December, just a few days after Pearl Harbor. And here they were in the Philippines the following March.

"During the time we were assembling the planes, Japanese reconnaissance aircraft passed overhead often and at odd hours. After the first few scares we realized that they couldn't see us through the trees. As soon as we cut trees to allow pushing the planes the few hundred feet to the single-lane gravel road which paralleled the beach, the Japanese would probably spot us. So we waited until the night before we intended to fly the planes out. Then, with lots of help from the Filipinos, we cleared our 'taxiway.'

"Each day almost on schedule, a four-engine Japanese flying boat passed over right at noon, always coming from the same direction, and flying a straight line course. We called him Photo Charlie. Scheduled to fly the first plane out was our senior pilot, Lt. Warden. Even though we were ready at 10:30 a.m., he kept stalling and checking and waiting. We suspected that he was worried about flying off the narrow gravel road.

"Actually, he was waiting for something. He took off just before noon with no problem. Warden took off, turned out to sea, and disappeared. He hadn't been gone ten minutes when we heard the drone of Photo Charlie. We thought that if Warden had been just a bit later, he might have gone after him. Just as Charlie was overhead, we heard the high-pitched scream of a diving fighter, and out of the sun and firing came our P-40. His dive carried him under Charlie, and as he pulled up under him, Warden fired again. Charlie was burning and crashed in the mountains about 10 miles away. Next day our Filipino friends brought souvenirs from Charlie, whose meticulous timetable had cost the Japanese a large airplane and crew."

With Friends Like This

Bob Hoover, who in 1949 came to Allison's Flight Test operations, has a P-40 "combat" story with a twist:

With about 2,000 more airframes to come, the 15,000th P-40 Warhawk bears insignia of many U.S. and Allied air force units in which its sister ships served. The plane was photographed near the Curtiss-Wright plant in Buffalo, New York, in November 1944.

"[While I was in flight training] during September 1942 in St. Petersburg, Florida, we lost a P-40 because of an engine problem, rumored to have been some sort of bearing, and a fellow had bailed out. Soon afterward six of us in a P-40 V-formation were diving on water slicks marked with irridescent dye for target practice. We had tracers to help us get the feel of the thing, and we went round in a rectangular pattern, then dove, shot, and pulled up. I was starting down on my run and had no more triggered my guns than suddenly my engine was on fire. "Oh, oh," I thought, "it's those bearings." So I pulled up but couldn't get high enough to bail out. So I opened up the canopy and headed for the beach and ditched it.

"My commanding officer landed on the beach in a little plane, maybe a Cub. A nearby fishing boat picked me up. The CO asked me what was wrong, and I said, 'Engine failure. It caught fire and I shut everything off and ditched.' The next day we returned, and in the shallow water we could see the ship sitting on the bottom. They fished it out and it was full of .50 calibre bullet holes. The fellow behind me was concentrating on the target and just didn't see me, and shot me full of holes."

Lucky Lightning

Of all the Allison-powered aircraft of World War II, none was more glamorous nor more successful than Lockheed's P-38 Lightning. John Goldthwaite recalled a nervous afternoon when an early Lightning narrowly escaped possible disaster: "One of our first engines for the P-38 went through the full production run and somehow a faulty reduction gear pinion had been installed. After failure on the test stand, that reduction gear pinion was dead soft, worn halfway through, had somehow escaped the heat treatment. We had shipped two engines to Lockheed. So we stopped shipping them all right. We wired our

representative at Lockheed and told him to hold up installation of that engine. We invented an excuse so they wouldn't fly it until we'd looked at this thing. Then we telephoned him at his hotel and said, 'Now, the real reason is, you take the cover off that gear box and take a file and find out if those gear teeth are hard, because we found one gear that hadn't been hardened. You can tell with a file,' we said. 'And you report back to us right away.' Well, it turned out it was all right, so he put the gear box back together and Lockheed flew it and it was successful, and that was the start of the P-38."

At the height of wartime output in 1943, Lockheed's Burbank, California, P-38 production line made an impressive sight. Almost 10,000 Lightnings were built by war's end, accounting for a substantial portion of Allison's V1710 installations.

The heavily-armed P-39 made an excellent ground support fighter particularly popular with the Russian Air Force to whom thousands were flown via Alaska and Siberia. Pilots grumbled about the plane's cold cockpit: instead of helping to warm toes and fingers, the rear-mounted engine's external heat was largely shed uselessly into the slipstream.

Bottom: The Bell P-39 Airacobra was designed for a rear-mounted engine. The long shafting was vibration-damped with a hydraulic unit. The engine location permitted installation of a .37mm cannon that fired through the prop hub. Maintenance under camouflage nets in the South Pacific was photographed early in WWII.

The Wonders of Shafting

Before World War II, the primary company objective was to do everything possible with the V1710 engine. Chief engineer Ron Hazen became famous for his willingness to take on challenging projects—shafting, turbosupercharging, most anything. Larry Bell's designers came up with the P-39 Airacobra, with engine behind the pilot, requiring a uniquely complex installation.

Engineer Bill Emmick tells this story: "The first engine test lasted ten minutes because of a shaft failure in the accessories housing due to severe torsional vibration in the shaft and engine combination. Design engineer

Oscar Montieth and project manager Marshall Davis devised the first hydraulic dampener to handle the torsional vibration, and more than 7,000 P-39s were flown across the Arctic to Russia without a single failure of engine or shaft."

One of World War II's finest fighters, the North American Aviation P-51 Mustang was designed for Britain's Royal Air Force. Based upon requirements set by the British Purchasing Commission in New York early in 1940, NAA president James H. "Dutch" Kindleberger and his design team in Inglewood, California, began design for the new fighter. The plane, designated NA73, was planned for high volume manufacture from the outset. Its many advanced elements included a laminar-flow wing based on NACA studies.

The design was finished and a prototype built in an astonishing 78,000 engineering hours in 127 days. Fitted with its Allison V1710, the P-51A first flew October 26, 1940. It soon achieved 382 mph at 14,000 ft, equal to the British Spitfire. but at higher altitudes its performance was limited by its lack of high altitude supercharging. Early Allsion-powered Mustangs performed with outstanding success in ground attack and intruder roles in northwest Europe in 1942-1944. Equipped with Packard-built Rolls-Royce Merlin engines specifically designed for high altitude, subsequent P-51Bs earned distinction as long-range escorts for heavy bombers.

Continued from page 74

The Peacetime Challenge Looms

As the crisis of the war yielded to predictions of victory for the Allied cause, General Motors executives were planning for a peacetime future that was surely just ahead.

For the corporation, the shift from the operational distortions of wartime would almost certainly benefit from rising demand for GM's long-established consumer products, from automobiles to refrigerators, but at Allison Ed Newill could anticipate no such ready markets. The very existence of his division since 1932 was inextricably linked to military aviation. The division's production of 70,000 V1710s and 10 million aircraft engine bearings were impressive proof of what the firm could accomplish. But with the abrupt termination of high-volume military contracts only a matter of time, Norman Gilman's early determination to have a viable product took on still greater urgency—if Allison were to survive beyond its initial great successes.

History had several surprises in store for Edward Newill and his staff at Jim Allison's thriving but precariously positioned enterprise. Among them lay a photograph in a general's desk drawer at Wright Field in Dayton.

Later P-51s were fitted with Packard-built Rolls-Royce Merlin engines. A sophisticated Aeroproducts four-bladed prop helped to provide some of the ship's legendary performance. Aeroproducts test pilot Raleigh Martin takes a break at the company's hangar at Dayton Municipal Airport sometime late in the war.

CHAPTER 6
Transitioning

*Planning for peacetime.
From pistons to jets; V1710 yields to
J33 and J35; how to price a jet engine.
Whittle and GE. Jet manufacturing,
setting records. Development and
volume manufacture conflict, the
Allison/GM anomaly. Markets of
opportunity; transmissions, bearings,
locomotive parts, shock absorbers. The
automatic transmission comes to
Indianapolis.*

Previous page: Designated the XB-39, the Boeing B-29 Superfortress at the Fisher Body Division at Romulus Field in Cleveland, Ohio, in 1944 during installation of 2,600-hp V3420-A16 engines and special nacelles. In the background are Fisher P-75 fighters.

Director of engineering Ron Hazen (center) shares jet engine production information with two influential visitors in 1946. Charles Wilson (left), whose recommendations influenced GM's acquisition of Allison in 1929, was GM president from 1941 to 1953, when he was named Dwight Eisenhower's Secretary of Defense. Alfred P. Sloan, Jr., (right) was GM president from 1923 to 1937, and chairman of the board from 1937 to 1956.

Corporations are like complex living organisms, with distinctive characteristics, unique personalities. Their destinies are shaped by the people who lead them, by the forces of history, and even the whimsy of fate.

Allison is no exception. From the comparative spontaneity and flexibility of its early days, the company at the end of World War II found itself of a size and in a place not entirely of its own choosing. That situation would recur in the late 1970s, but at the end of WWII, Allison's leaders strove to rebalance the company and its resources to survive in a radically-changed environment.

A View from Detroit

The long-term strategy for each of its divisions received careful consideration from General Motors management. Allison's postwar adjustment was but one, if unique, among many challenges facing the corporation. GM had, after all, radically altered the shape and conduct of almost every facet of its operation to meet the wartime emergency. Observed GM chairman Alfred Sloan: "Only a small proportion of GM products have wartime applications. When we were mobilized during WWII, we were obliged to transform the great bulk of our operations almost completely, to learn rapidly and under great pressure how to produce tanks, machine guns, aircraft propellers, and many other kinds of equipment with which we had no experience at all." During the war, GM produced $12 billion worth of military goods, and between February 1942 and September 1945, built no passenger cars in the U.S.

Wartime GM Policy Making

Under chairman Sloan and president Charles E. "Engine Charley" Wilson, GM had devised a wartime decision-making structure that included a three-member Policy Committee (Wilson and executive vice presidents Bradley and Hunt) to handle all operations policies. The 14-member War Administration Committee directed all war operations for the duration.

In his 1942 report to the Postwar Planning Group that became the basis for GM's aviation program, Sloan called out three major markets: commercial air transport, private civilian flying, and the military. Even with great expansion of commercial flying, sales potential for a single aircraft manufacturer was likely to be limited, said the report; safety hazards then inherent in small planes would limit the private flying market as compared to the automobile; and the military market was seen as likely to be both limited and highly technical—and therefore expensive.

Allison and GM Aviation Prospects

In August 1943 the GM policy committee had concluded an analysis of the corporation's role in aviation with two policy decisions. First, the corporation should not produce complete airframes in either the military or transport areas. This thinking led GM to sell its interests in Bendix and North American in 1948. Second, the corporation "should develop as complete a position on the manufacture of accessories as its capacity and circumstances make possible."

Those decisions were consistent with Detroit's attitudes towards the Allison Division articulated by Sloan: "First, to manufacture complete airplanes would jeopardize the other aviation business of the corporation. The Allison Division was, and would continue to be, a major producer of airplane engines and aircraft accessories applicable with minor variations to many kinds of planes and might normally account for 40 percent of the cost of the complete airplane. Such a manufacturer would need the confidence of the aircraft manufacturers, not to be a competitor." And second, "We do research in our fields of competence, but we are largely a production organization."

The Allison Flexibility

During 1944 Ed Newill's concern for Allison's future took him frequently to Detroit for planning sessions with GM group vice president Bob Evans. Evans launched a survey of other divisions to assess the matching of their potential peacetime needs with the enormous manufacturing capacity soon to be freed at Allison. Among suitable prospects were shock absorbers for Delco, blowers for Detroit Diesel, and hydraulic lift pumps for International Harvester. Plant 3, the original Allison production plant, would be converted and tooled for the manufacture of these commercial products.

Grander tasks were in the making, but these options would serve as excellent interim products to maintain a core of fiscal stability. Not the least of those products were the gears, bearings, and other precision components that flowed north to a busy factory just outside Chicago.

The Railroad Coupling

Having laid the groundwork with substantial research and development work on diesel engines in the 1930s, General Motors assumed unchallenged postwar dominance in the massive switch of America's railroads from steam to diesel power. All across the land, the thunder and hiss of the iron horse yielded to the steady throb of powerful,

With many of their precision components built at Allison plants, GM's Electro-Motive Division diesel locomotives began to dominate American railroading immediately after WWII. During the 1950s the handsome E and F-series units, often painted in vivid liveries, headed most of the nation's passenger and freight trains. Striking in deep orange, forest green, and metallic gold striping, these 1,500-hp F-7 A and B passenger units were built at EMD's La Grange shops for Great Northern in 1952.

economical diesel locomotives. Most of the sleek and colorful new engines first saw daylight in La Grange, Illinois. They bore the stylish nameplate of the Electro-Motive Division of General Motors.

So highly regarded were EMD locomotives for their quality and performance, that leading railroad historian S. Kip Farrington wrote in 1949, "In fact, it is my opinion that there would be few other Diesels ordered than those produced by Electro-Motive if this concern could turn them out fast enough."

The Electro-Motive Engineering Corporation, incorporated in August 1922 in Cleveland, Ohio, was acquired by GM in 1930. The three million-square-foot La Grange factory was built in 1935, and most of the modern procedures and systems for mass production of standardized railway locomotives were pioneered there. Allison became a core supplier of major components, from bearings to gears, for the hundreds of locomotives that rolled ceaselessly from La Grange during the late 1940s and into the 1950s.

An Orderly Mess

Even with all this planning, the suddenness of the end of the war made an orderly transition to peacetime operations impossible. It took 9,000 freight carloads just to haul away GM's military inventory, another 8,000 to dispose of government equipment and machinery. "Meanwhile," wrote chairman Sloan, "we were rushing to equip our plants for commercial production. Altogether there was a mess but no confusion."

Values and Allison's Search for Direction

For Allison, of course, no loyal customers were flocking showrooms eager to snap up new models.

Among Ed Newill's special worries were the futures of Allison's 20,000 employees, for whom only about 4,600 jobs would be available by January 1946. Understandably, a high percentage of the peak work force were people eager to return to their pre-war occupations on the farms and in neighboring communities. But Allison was an important focus for many skilled and experienced employees, including a portion of the 3,538 Allison men who had been drafted into the armed services by December 1943.

In Indianapolis, Allison management choices dealt pragmatically and sensibly with immediate problems and short-term solutions, but always with an eye to the big opportunity if and when it might develop. In fact, the aggregate wisdom of many relatively small decisions would facilitate not simply survival but considerable prosperity. Along with common sense, key elements of Allison's success after 1945 continued to be sound engineering, a willingness to tackle unusual technical problems, devotion to quality, and a consistent commitment to seeing a project through to user satisfaction that was not lost in the marketplace. On more than one occasion, the well-earned Allison reputation for integrity would help to buoy the company through difficulties.

An Interruption

In April 1945 when the Army Air Forces terminated Allison's V1710 volume production, the company was forced to lay off all but 2,600 bargaining unit employees. On November 19, 1945, the local, along with locals in other GM plants across the nation struck to regain wages lost as a result of wartime freezes. The union calculated that its members were an average of 30 cents per hour behind on wages.

The strike continued until March 23, 1946, and among the settlement offer conditions were an 18.5-cent-per-hour increase and some additional fringe benefits. During the early phase of the stoppage, management moved key administrative offices into a downtown hotel. Bargaining unit employees refused to enter the plants, of course, and salaried employees were shut out, except for the Protection Service staff.

Railway and Teamster unions supported the strike, refusing to deliver shipments. In December a court injunction allowed salary workers back into the plants. In an unanticipated side effect of the stoppage, more than a few managers and engineers reported that enforced time away from pressures of that turbulent time provided welcome opportunities to concentrate on technical and managerial innovations.

No Reasonable Offer Refused

While Newill shored up Allison with his network of supplementary production for other divisions, and undertook the launch of commercial and military transmissions, the aviation people were not diverted from their true calling. No success came easily. Allison aero engineers and managers went through dozens of prototypes for each winning product or installation.

Until 1946 when Ralph Golt and Bill Gage put together the nucleus of a sales department to solicit commercial applications, the installation engineers took the company's wares to the customer, whether military or airframe builders. "We were half salesman, half engineer," recalled James E. "Jim" Knott (who would become Allison general manager and a GM vice president). Taking the initiative was a major Allison tactic. "We often would design an unsolicited installation for a particular airframe and take it to the builder to inspire them. Harry Karcher (later to lead major Allison projects) and I in Indianapolis would assemble some hypothetical designs from our stable of components for an appealing airplane, then I'd take them out to companies and say, 'Here's what you can do.'"

Displayed in February 1946 at Northwest Airlines' Michigan Avenue ticket office in Chicago, the XB-42 propulsion layout shows the large gearbox that permitted independent prop operation. To the left can be seen a drawing of a proposed Douglas passenger plane application of the drive scheme—the original DC-4—that was not pursued. The Mixmaster Rockettes are Northwest staffers.

Two 1,425-hp V1710-E23Bs, located in the top of the fuselage and connected to the remote gearbox with 30-foot drive shafts, drove pusher-type, counter-rotating props in the tail cone of the 1945 Douglas XB-42 Mixmaster light bomber.. The advent of jet engines terminated the project.

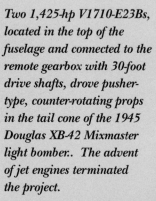

In 1945 the Fisher Aircraft Development activity was closed and several engineers transferred to Allison to form the Installation Engineering Section whose objective was to sell engines for commercial applications. Said Knott, "We studied adaptations of 1710 engines, and later turbines, to almost every commercial aircraft then being considered."

Projects that did not see production included the Douglas B-42 in which two V1710 engines mounted in the fuselage drove

counter-rotating propellers in the tail through 27 feet of shafting. Inevitably nicknamed the Mixmaster, the XB-42 used fail-safe gearing so that counter-rotation was maintained even with one engine out. Under chief engineer Ed Burton, the Douglas design staff also projected an enlarged version of the B-42 as a commercial transport—the original DC-4 design idea—but airline buyers resisted both the unconventional layout and the liquid-cooled engines. The airlines were no more receptive to the idea of V1710s for the Douglas DC-6, for which Don Berlin prepared a complete nacelle design.

An opportunity to reengine Boeing's B-17 Flying Fortress with the F series V1710 engines was lost in Southern California's Tehachapi mountains. In 1943 Air Force General Don Putt was concerned to improve the B-17's performance and to provide an alternative in case of shortages of its Wright R-1820 radial engines. At Putt's suggestion, Lockheed's Vega division, which had manufactured nearly 3,000 Flying Fortresses under license in Burbank, designed a V1710 nacelle for a B-17 test airplane, the XB-38. During May tests the plane verified the expected performance improvements. But on a flight over Bakersfield a fire developed, the crew abandoned ship, and the prototype crashed.

Another attempt came, this time to fit the V3420 to Boeing's B-29 Superfortress, designated the XB-39. Don Berlin, whose first Allison collaboration was as Curtiss' chief P-40 designer, and who had designed

Engineer Don Berlin, who had been Curtiss' chief designer for the P-40 before coming to Indianapolis to head up Allison flight test operations, led such programs as the V3420 nacelle for the XB-39 and the proposed V1710 installation for the Douglas DC-6 passenger liner.

In May 1943 an experimental installation of 1,425-hp V1710-F17 engines was made in a Boeing B-17E Flying Fortress. Performance of the resulting XB-38 was superior to the radial engine plane, but interrupting Boeing's production to tool up for a new variant was determined to be excessively time-consuming.

Above: T he XB-39, A Boeing B-29 Superfortress airframe, makes an early test flight with her V3420s newly-installed in winter 1944-45.

Center, right: Allison's chief test pilot for many years, B.T. "Red" Hulse prepares for a test flight during 1945 in a Fisher XP-75, whose counter-rotating Aeroproducts propellers were driven by the Allison V3240 engine.

Facing, bottom: In 1939 Douglas built the 160,000-lb XB-19, the world's largest land plane, with a wing span of 212 ft. The plane was used as a flying laboratory, and among her assignments was testing of Allison V3420 nacelles for the XB-39 in 1944.

the XB-19A installation and the Fisher XP-75, came from GM's Detroit Aircraft Development section to head the installation department at Allison's Plant 10 assisted by Bill Watson. Jim Knott was assigned to Berlin's group as chief powerplant engineer and supervised design and construction of the XB-39 nacelle in the GM Styling Section building on Milwaukee Avenue.

Like Riding a Bicycle

The XB-39 nacelle was first flight-tested, on the Douglas XB-19A testbed airplane, in December 1944. The flight was memorable on several counts, not the least of which was its unorthodox crew. Recalled

Knott, "I remember that flight very well because on that day the assigned flight engineer had come down with the flu, and Colonel Ernie Warburton, the Army Air Force test pilot, was going to postpone the flight. I brashly announced that I had been a flight engineer on Pan American's Boeing 314 flying boats, and had worked on the installation of these engines. Since I knew the controls and systems well, I could fly as flight engineer. Of course I was thrilled, but when Allison and GM learned of my volunteering, they promptly grounded me, saying that they hadn't hired me to do experimental flight testing." The project, too, was grounded as the war drew to a close.

The Douglas XB-19, then the largest bomber in the world, was characterized by engineer Al Sobey as "an overgrown, four-engine DC-3 with a span over 200 feet. The wings were so thick that I could crawl out to read the instruments mounted behind the outboard engines."

The Turbine Touchstone

Even while Allison bent its every energy during WWII to building V1710s and planned when it could for peacetime, once again an engine designed under the pressures of world war was being readied for history and a significant role in the Allison story.

Soon after the U.S. entered the war, epochal advances in turbine technology in Germany, Italy, and England became cause for real concern to American military leaders, particularly Deputy Chief of Staff for Air, General Henry H. "Hap" Arnold. On February 25, 1941, Arnold asked National Advisory Committee for Aeronautics chairman Vannevar Bush to appoint a special committee on jet propulsion whose purpose would be to coordinate early U.S. acquisition of jet engine capabilities.

In March the group was named. It was headed by Will Durand, with representatives from the Army Air Forces, the National Bureau of Standards, Johns Hopkins University, Massachusetts Institute of Technology, and three firms with reputations in steam and gas turbine

Famed for his farsighted vision and called by some "the father of the U.S. Air Force," Gen. Hap Arnold no sooner learned of Frank Whittle's revolutionary jet engine in 1941 than he acted decisively to acquire its technology for the U.S. With a P-38 behind them, Arnold confers with Lockheed Aircraft Corporation president Robert Gross and an aide in Burbank in November 1944.

work—Allis Chalmers, General Electric, and Westinghouse. GE was particularly respected by the military because of its leadership, dating to World War I, in turbosupercharger development. Arnold specifically excluded the major manufacturers of reciprocating engines—Allison, Pratt & Whitney, and Curtiss-Wright—because the three firms were fully occupied with wartime production of reciprocating engines.

Frank Whittle's Engine

In Britain, Frank Whittle's W-1X centrifugal compressor jet engine had first run in December 1940 and flew, in the Gloster E.28/39, on May 15, 1941. Arnold was invited by the British Air Ministry to observe the Gloster perform a few days later. He returned to Washington determined to get a U.S. jet engine moving with no further delay. He asked GE engineering vice president R.C. Muir to confer with the military to review the British engine project under terms of an agreement signed by U.S. Secretary of War Henry Stimson and Sir Henry Self of the British Air Commission, by which the Whittle technology would be made available on condition of rigorous secrecy.

Arnold and senior Army Air Force officers met with four General Electric managers and worked out an agreement under which GE would build 15 of the Whittle engines. Larry Bell, president of Bell Aircraft in Buffalo, New York, was informed the next day that his company was to build an airframe for the new engine.

The British Are Coming

The British drawings that arrived at GE's River Works in Lynn, Massachusetts, proved a bit cryptic and incomplete in some areas. The British obliged by sending a sample engine and three technicians to aid the GE engineers. On April 18, 1942, GE's Type I-A (pronounced "eye"-A) engine ran successfully. Whittle himself came to the U.S. (staying in Boston under an assumed name) in June 1942 to provide advice and counsel as the engine was being readied for installation in the Bell airplane. On October 2, 1942, Bell's XP-59A Airacomet, piloted by Bell's Bob Stanley, at Muroc Dry Lake, California, made America's first jet-powered flight.

Yes, But What Is it?

Several Allison episodes have, with the years, assumed mythic status, to recur in the archives, in the memories of participants, and as hearsay with remarkable consistency. Such a tale is that of Allison's introduction to Whittle's invention. The classic version follows:

"In June 1944 Ed Newill was visiting Wright Field, home of the Air Materiel Command. Allison had just finished its 50,000th V1710, and government funding for new Allison test flight facilities at Plant 10 had been approved. D-Day was in the papers. Walking down the hall, Allison's general manager heard: 'Mr. Newill, will you step in here a minute?' From a desk drawer, a senior procurement man took a photo. 'Can you make this for us?' 'Aircraft engines are our business,' replied Newill looking at the photographs, 'If that's what you want, we will make them. It is a jet engine, isn't it?' 'Yes, and we would like to have your firm price and production schedule in one week.'

"'That's not much time,' replied Newill. 'I know, but we need these in the worst sort of way.' 'Can we have a model and prints shipped to Allison?' 'There is no model,' interrupted the procurement man. 'A set of prints?' 'The blueprints are not complete as the design is not finished.'

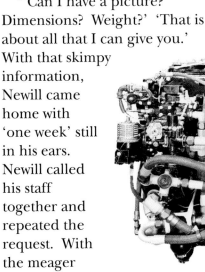

"'Can I have a picture? Dimensions? Weight?' 'That is about all that I can give you.' With that skimpy information, Newill came home with 'one week' still in his ears. Newill called his staff together and repeated the request. With the meager information in hand, a detailed study was clearly impossible. After lengthy discussion, someone said: 'If we know how much it weighs, let's take the cost per pound of our present engine and apply that to the weight of the new engine, and give them that as the price.' No one had a better idea.

"A week later Newill returned to Wright Field with a firm price quote and a delivery schedule. Allison got the order and delivered its first engine on schedule within 10 percent of the original price quotation."

This Is What It Is

No one at Allison had anything beyond theoretical knowledge of the principles of jet propulsion in 1944, but they learned quickly in spite of secrecy precautions that were occasionally vexing.

Sworn to silence, a small group of engineers and manufacturing technicians visited the General Electric plant in Lynn. Among the group was John Goldthwaite, who recalled GE's superb cooperation warmly and the secrecy wryly: "Building 29 was the holy of holies of the project, so secret that my pass didn't even carry the name of the building. The GE people told me that they had trouble getting started because when the drawings first came over, nobody was authorized to open the three

In its earliest practical form, the turbojet employed a single centrifugal compressor that required the large circumference displayed by this early Allison production model J33 shown around 1945. Air intake is from the left end through the compressor; fuel (kerosene) was injected into the gas stream where it was ignited in the combustion chambers that angle in to the turbine stages, and then to the exhaust.

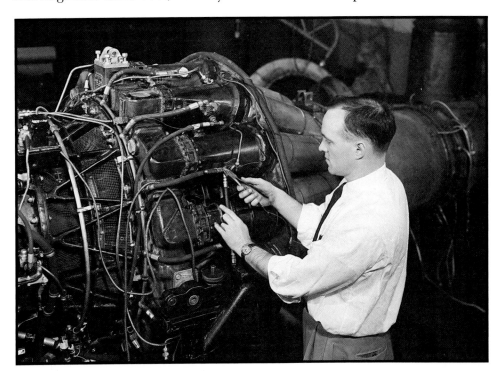

While an engineer trims a securing wire, several features of this early J33 can be seen, including the front mounting of accessories on the "W" support structure. Through the screened air inlets at the left, the front of the compressor guide vanes are visible.

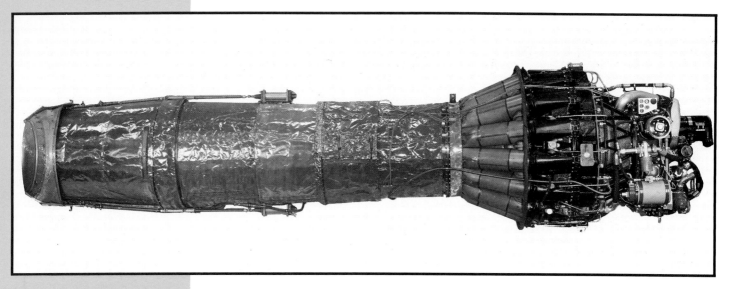

Viewed from the right side is the first of the production afterburning jets, the J33-A-33 of 1947. The afterburner, fitted in the turbojet's tailpipe, permits injection of additional fuel into the gas stream where its ignition provides increased thrust. This unit was used for the engine's 150-hour test.

In this 1947 production view with the engine vertically suspended nose down in the assembly stand, the J33 combustion chambers ("burner cans") and the first-stage turbine wheel blades (sometimes called "buckets") can be seen at the top. Vertical assembly helped to assure stability in rotating components and provided better lighting and access during manufacture.

seals—separate ones for the Army, the Navy, and the State Department. The State Department couldn't break Army or Navy seals, and neither the Army nor the Navy could break the State Department seal. They actually had to send those drawings back and get another set with only one seal before they were able even to see the drawings."

Back in Maywood, things went more smoothly. A study group of about 20 technicians, tooling men mostly, and one engineer met in a locked room upstairs in Plant 5. They studied the project to decide what had to be done, what tools had to be bought, and what procedures had to be followed to build the engine. The materials were specified on the drawings—but in GE numbers that had to be translated for interpretation. Continued Goldthwaite, "We were strictly forbidden to make any changes. Our engine had to be completely interchangeable with the GE at first, and they retained complete design responsibility. Any modification we wanted to make we had to clear through the General Electric plant at Lynn. And in turn, they had to clear through General Electric top headquarters at Schenectady."

The project at first included two basic engines, both centrifugal flow—the original I-16 (derived from the Whittle design) which generated 1,600 lbs of thrust, and the GE-designed, 4,000-lb-thrust I-40 (based on knowledge derived from Whittle's work) that became the J33. Allison had originally been invited into the jet engine business as a

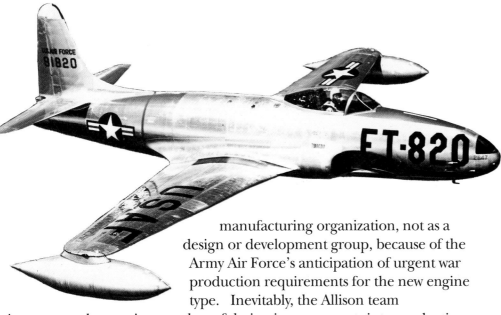

manufacturing organization, not as a design or development group, because of the Army Air Force's anticipation of urgent war production requirements for the new engine type. Inevitably, the Allison team incorporated a growing number of design improvements into production engines, and as the I-40 matured into the J33, Allison ultimately manufactured 15,525, primarily for Lockheed's F-80, F-94 and T-33; Grumman's F9F; Chance Vought's Regulus missile; and Martin's B-61 Matador. The first Allison J33 was delivered February 3, 1945.

The next phase of U.S. turbine engine development came with GE's introduction of the axial-flow TG-100/T31 engine in the 4,000-lb-thrust class. The Air Force chose to fund continued development and production of both engines. General Motors was asked to take on production responsibilities for the TG-100/T31, now designated the J35, as well.

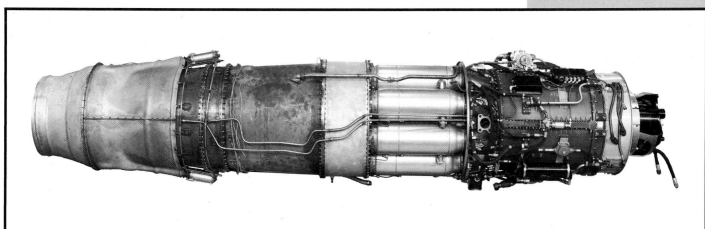

Another Kelley Johnson airplane, Lockheed's F-80 Shooting Star carried the jet engine from exotic breakthrough into day-after-day practicality, setting records on the way. As America's first operational jet fighter, Allison-powered F-80s dominated Korean skies during the early days of the Korean War. In a dual-seat arrangement, the airframe later became the T-33 trainer in which an entire generation of USAF pilots entered the jet age.

Some of the Allison godfathers who nurtured the J33 into production, from left are T.S. McCrae, J.B. Wheatley, Fred Luker, Charlie McDowall, A.W.F. Green, W.C. Oestrike, J.C. Fetters, and R.P. Atkinson.

In December 1946 Allison built its first J35 jet engine, and its slender profile reveals the new compressor arrangement that has been standard for jet engine cores since. The more efficient axial layout allowed engine and plane designers greater flexibility of engine performance and installation options.

Testing of rotating parts was vital to jet engine development, particularly for compressor and turbine wheels with their complex castings. Turbine wheels were subject to both high rotation speeds and temperatures that significantly affected their metallic structure. A J33 compressor wheel is lowered into a sub-floor spin chamber for test. High-pressure steam provided the immensely high rotation speeds.

The first J35 was flight tested in February 1946—in a Republic XP-84. Because Allison itself was seen as fully involved in the J33, volume J35 production was assigned to Chevrolet's Tonawanda, New York, factory.

In 1947, as Chevrolet resumed full-scale auto production, J35 production was moved to Indianapolis, where Allison's growing expertise with turbine technology and available production capacity made an excellent match. General Electric, meanwhile, was developing the J47, and in the absence of Air Force direction of manufacturing resources, GE and Allison ceased their technology exchange and assumed the traditional roles of commercial competitors.

The New Turbine Universe

For Allison's aviation people, the new jets brought the sort of technical challenge on which they thrived. The J33 turbine wheel, for example, required a particularly hard steel that had to be machined on both sides in a very large lathe recalling the pre-production days of the V1710.

Perhaps the most severe problem, John Goldthwaite reported, was "the turbine wheels which ran practically red hot on the rim and at very high speed. Now and then a wheel would blow up on the test stand. We gathered up the pieces and tried to find the flaw, but we couldn't. GE was having the same problem. Our chief metallurgist, Arthur Green, finally made a metallurgical study with a history of every single forging including the particular mold at the steel mill, the particular ingot that was involved, and the particular position in the billet—the preliminary forging made from an ingot cast right out of the furnace. We found out that every broken wheel had come from the bottom of the ingot even after trimming of the accepted 20%. After they cut about 10 percent more off the bottom of the ingot, there never was a broken wheel."

An Occasional Chuckle

While Allison and GE mastered the manufacture of the new engines, jet aircraft began to make their way in the world. Early flights of Bell's XP-59 jet were all made in great secrecy. Even though he was working closely with both Bell and Curtiss in Buffalo at the time, Jim Knott knew nothing about the jet flights. But it wasn't long before the airplane drew public notice, reported Knott. "The airplanes were flown out of Niagara Falls and the test pilot was Jack Woolams, who soon found out that no one had ever seen an airplane flying without a propeller. The test flight area was adjacent to American Airlines' DC-3 flight path from Buffalo to New York. So Jack got a tall opera hat and a curved pipe. He'd put the hat on and the pipe in his mouth and fly up alongside the DC-3 and very slowly pass on by. Soon stories appeared in the local press describing a pilot with top hat, curved pipe and a propellerless plane."

From Oddity to Workhorse

In early 1946, jet engine time between overhaul (TBO) was set at 50 hours. Few operated that long, but by year end, the J33 achieved 100 hours TBO. Confidence in jet engines grew among designers, builders, pilots, and maintenance men. Early in 1947, water-alcohol injection gave the J33 additional power for takeoff. The J35 went into production at Allison rated at 4,000 pounds thrust. In May 1947 the J33 completed the first turbine engine 150-hour qualification test ever, meeting the same standard of dependability then demanded of reciprocating engines. Turbine engines had come of age.

Whether at 40,000 feet or on the ramp in Alaska, Air Force jets must perform well at low temperatures. Allison's cold chamber test cell provided the opportunity to see that they would. A J33 is prepared for a run.

Next, the Record Book

For more than 20 years the world speed record for straight-away flight had been kept in Europe, but Kelly Johnson's F-80 Shooting Star and its Allison J33 were about to make history. Lockheed turned over a production airplane to the Fight Test Base at Muroc Dry Lake, and on June 19, 1947, the F-80R streaked across the measured course for the new world speed mark of 623.8 mph.

A few weeks later an Allison J35 teamed with a Douglas D-558 Skystreak to achieve 640.7 mph, and five days later, 650.6 mph. Impressive statistics accumulated to validate both the technology and Allison's production mastery of the jet engine. In May, 1946, 25 J33-powered F-80s flew en masse from March Field, California, to Washington, D.C.—the first mass jet flight in history.

In July, 1948, 15 J33-powered F-80s made the first mass jet flight across the Atlantic Ocean from Selfridge Air Force Base to Dow Field through Greenland, Iceland, Scotland, England, and on to Furstenfeldbruck, Germany. The J33 also powered the first flight of a U.S. jet missile, the Martin Matador.

The Type Certificate

In early 1948 the J33-23 came into production. In April, the first Air Force group to be equipped with the J35-powered Republic F-84 Thunderjets was activated. In May the first jet engine approved for commercial use—the J33 developed and built by Allison—obtained CAA

One of the J35's important installations was in the Republic F-84 Thunderjet. Equipped for mid-air refueling, fleets of F-84s made transoceanic delivery flights to overseas air bases across both the Atlantic and Pacific from 1950. An F-84G is refueled from a converted Boeing B-29 in the spring of 1952. The long overwater flights helped verify the jet engine's growing dependability.

approval, its
ATC type-
certificate.

In fall 1948 a Northrop YB-49 Flying Wing
powered by eight J35 engines flew nonstop more than 3,400
miles for a new distance record for jet aircraft, at an average
speed of 382 mph. By 1949, Allison had begun development of a new
high thrust engine, the J71. That same year marked Allison's delivery of
its 5,000th jet engine to U.S. Air Force. Through redesign and
production economies, the cost of J33 and J35 engines continued to
shrink. The original price of $55,000 for the J33 was down to less than
$20,000 by 1947 and the J35 which had started at $44,000 was at $36,900
in 1949.

The V1710 Last Hurrah

Allison met the final requirement for V1710 engines by producing 750
engines for the North American F-82 Twin Mustang, the last Air Force
fighter to be powered with reciprocating engines. With the conclusion of
that contract in December 1947, all further reciprocating engine
development was halted.

The First Allison Transmissions

Allison's steady progress in the air was matched by parallel
developments on the ground, and even before Pearl Harbor, the
foundation for what would ultimately become another Allison division
was being laid in Detroit.

In response to a request from the Army Ordnance Department for an
improved battle tank transmission, the first Torqmatic crossdrive
transmission had been conceived in 1941 by GM Product Study Group
Number 3 under engineering vice president Ormand Hunt and headed
by Oliver Kelley. The unit, designed for engine input of 850 hp, coupled
a torque converter to a powershift three-speed and reverse
transmission—technology completely new to heavy vehicle operation.
After extensive continued development to incorporate provisions for
vehicle steering and braking, and simple operator controls, by 1944 the
revolutionary CD-850 was ready for pilot testing.

Late that year, Allison managers, including chief designer Charlie
McDowall, met with Kelley and his group to explore Allison involvement
in refinement and manufacture of the unit. The project looked attractive
to everybody. In November GM group vice president Bob Evans and
Allison general manager Ed Newill proposed the new transmission to the
Army with the understanding that Allison would be the prime contractor.
The proposal was accepted, and in February 1945 the "B96 Transmission
Engineering Section" was established in Indianapolis within the Aircraft
Engineering Department. The embryo staff included engineers

Two of Northrop's fifteen 172-ft-span XB-35 propeller-driven Flying Wing strategic bombers were converted to YB-49 configuration with eight J35 engines during 1947. Shown during a 1948 test flight at Edwards AFB, California, is the No. One YB-49. The ship was destroyed on March 15, 1950, when the nose gear collapsed and the ship flipped over during a high-speed taxi run. No one was hurt in the incident.

In April 1949 the Allison staff began design of the high-thrust J71, retaining the diameter of the J35. Among aircraft powered with the engine were the Douglas B-66, the McDonnell F-3H, and the Northrop YF-89E, all in 1954.

Facing, bottom: Much as the V1710 established Allison as a major player in the world of military aero engines, so did the CD-850 cross-drive tank transmission position the company to become the preeminent maker of heavy-duty transmissions for the U.S. Army Ordnance Department. Conceived in 1941, the CD-850 prototype began testing in 1944 and reached production in 1949.

John Storer, U.A. Breting, P.B. Pritchard, and T. Bertrand; a secretary, and a single clerk.

The First Commercial Transmissions

As the end of the war approached, Robert M. Schaefer, a transmission and power train development engineer with GM's Detroit Transmission Division, submitted a proposal to his division general manager, V.A. Olsen, suggesting a series of Torqmatic transmissions to correspond with the Detroit Diesel Engine Division's line of engines for use in trucks, tractors, road machinery, boats, and off-highway applications. Olsen, an ex-Cadillac executive facing enormous demand for Hydramatic transmissions that completely filled capacity of his available plant, passed the proposal along to Bob Evans, group executive of the GM engine divisions. In Schaefer's proposal Evans saw the makings of an attractive match with the military transmission project already underway with Allison. GM's work with the Ordnance Department on cross-drives looked promising indeed, and the whole universe of heavy commercial vehicles had begun to seem like fertile ground for new transmission technology. Substantial production capability remained at the Allison Division in Indianapolis even with jet engine development and component production for other divisions.

After reviewing Schaefer's proposal, Evans wasted no time in asking the creative engineer to visit. "Schaefer, this is exactly what I want and I want you to get it for me." Evans had Schaefer transferred to Detroit Diesel with instructions to start a product study group for transmissions under Larry Sheldrick, director of engineering there. Evans chose marine gears as the first target market, and the first powershift marine gear was designed and pilot units fabricated there. The production responsibility was assigned to Allison, and Schaefer was transferred to Allison in September 1946.

Allison chief engineer Ron Hazen had already expanded the transmission section in April, naming Roy Lynch as chief engineer and Storer assistant chief for ordnance projects. Schaefer's new commercial projects made a perfect addition.

Parallel Division Components

In 1946 the Allison Division was divided into two separate operations under general manager Ed Newill. With reasonably-defined goals for Aircraft Operations and Transmission Operations, Allison was poised for the next stage of its development.

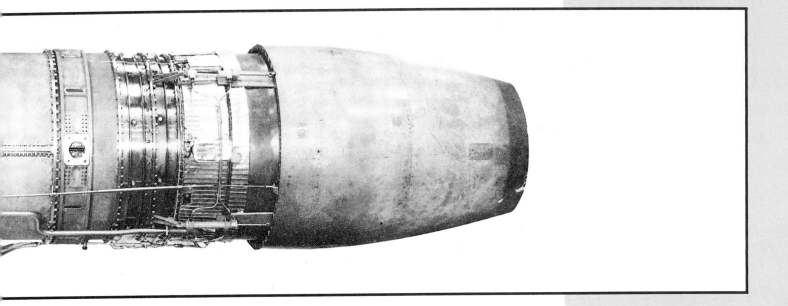

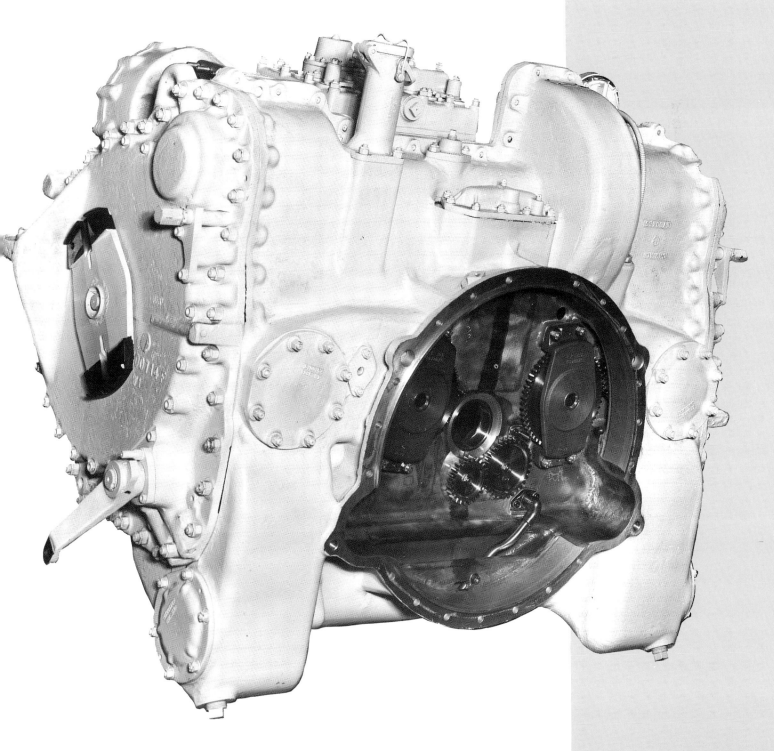

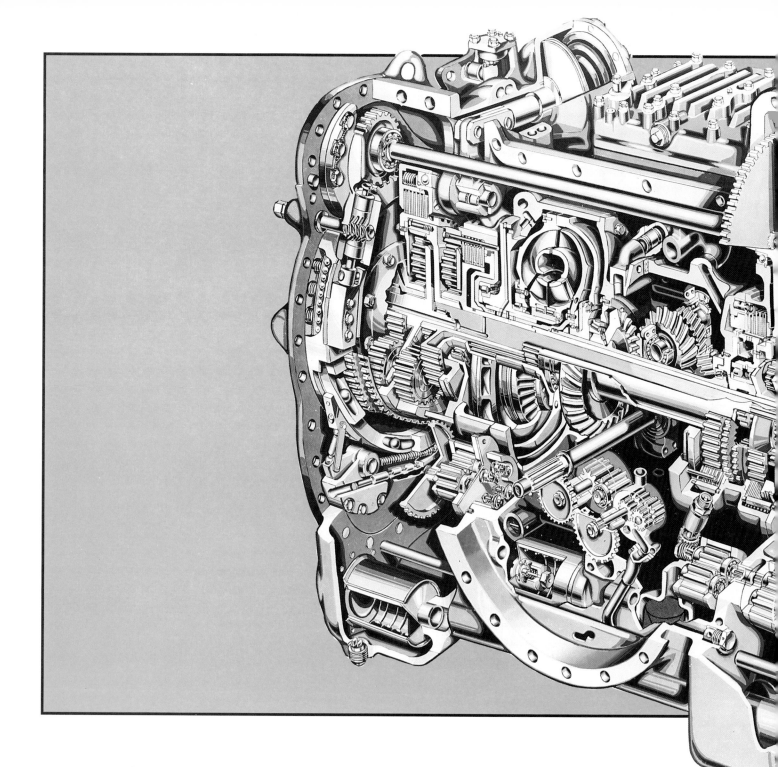

CHAPTER 7
Diversifying

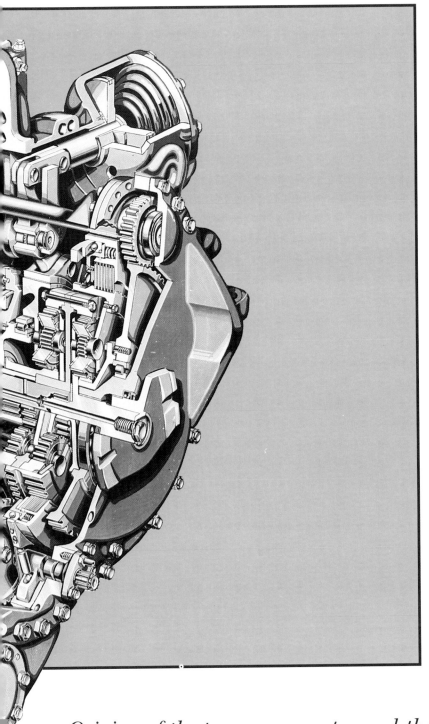

Origins of the torque converter and the
automatic transmission.
Product Study Group No. 3:
Crossdrives, Torqmatics, Powershifts,
and Marine Gears.
Building the Transmission Teams.
"Other Products." The V-drive.
A Mystery Transmission.
Going off-highway. The Rail Car.
The Cleveland Army Tank Plant.
A Cross-drive Dynasty.

Modern automatic transmission technology descends from two inventions that first saw practical application in the mid-1930s. Both use the properties of fluids in motion to transmit power from a source—usually an internal combustion engine—to some useful work, commonly the operation of a vehicle drive train.

Fluid Foundations

The first invention was the torque converter, essentially a fluid coupling attached to an engine, that permits smooth conversion of engine rotation, with degrees of variable torque output, to a transmission and drive shaft through rings of fixed (stators) and rotating (rotors) blades and vanes in a housing filled with oil. The torque converter was devised in its first industrial form in the mid-1930s by Alf Lysholm, then chief engineer for the Ljungstroms Company of Sweden.

Ljungstroms wasted no time in offering their proprietary technology under license. European licensees included Krupp in Germany and Leyland in Britain. In the U.S., Twin Disc was licensed for off-highway use and Spicer Manufacturing for trucks and highway vehicles.

The Ljungstroms converter unit was built up of sheet metal vanes. In the U.S., GM technicians would later supplant the costly sheet metal design with casting techniques they had perfected at their Bedford Foundry. Aluminum housings incorporating vanes and blades precision-cast through the lost-wax process provided quality and economy for the new transmission components.

The Protean Kelley Team

In Detroit, related General Motors developments followed at the Product Study Group and the Hydramatic and Detroit Diesel divisions. First came the Hydramatic, the first transmission with automatic shifts. The system included fluid coupling and an automatic four-speed transmission. Developed during the 1930s by the Product Study Group under O.E. Thompson and Oliver Kelley, it was first offered on a production car by Oldsmobile in 1940.

Advancing Tanks

The prototype CD-850 of 1944 followed two other GM tank transmission efforts. An early challenge had been the medium tank for which GM wanted to supply a torque converter and complete planetary gear transmission. The development process, however, went through several gear trains and took so long that the tank went into production with a synchromesh transmission.

Next came the M24 Chaffee light tank, designed and built by Cadillac. The M24's V-8 Cadillac engine had a Hydramatic transmission on each side, driving into a combining gearbox and steering differential, then out to the track sprockets. Although the drive train was exceedingly complicated, and there were control difficulties, the system made a lively and useful vehicle.

The cutaway model of the Torqmatic TC 500 of 1955 reveals the rugged structure— exemplified by the large ball bearing races—needed to transfer power from engines in the 150- to 350-hp range. The pump element (light colored, at left) is fixed to the engine flywheel, the driven turbine to the output shaft at right.

The Oldsmobile models of 1940 were the first to offer fully automatic transmissions, the Hydramatic developed by GM's Product Study Group. The unit's fluid coupling and automatic four-speed transmission provided the design base for Allison's own line of automatic transmissions. Courtesy Oldsmobile History Center

Oliver Kelley and his group had recognized the untenable combination of a large clutch, manual shift transmission, steering differential, and brakes of the medium tank. They tackled the formidable task of combining torque converter, transmission, steering differential, and brakes into one compact unit. With automatic and semi-automatic transmissions only recently attempted even for passenger cars, the idea of automatics in the power ranges required in tanks was genuinely daring.

The prospective advantages for tank utility were compelling motivation. One lay in the crossdrive's capacity for pivot steer—the ability of the tank to turn around its own axis. With the conventional steering differential, a tank's tightest possible turn was around the vehicle's moving inside track, a very much larger turning circle. For driver training, operator proficiency, and drivetrain durability, the new transmission's simplicity of operation was also a major advance. And the radical performance improvements came with major space-saving in the crowded tank hull.

The first of Allison's commercial transmission product lines (433 units were built in 1946), more than 60,000 marine gear sets have been delivered for pleasure and work boats.

The Seeds of a CD Dynasty

The CD-850 was proposed to the Army late in 1944 and enthusiastically accepted on February 1, 1945. Several test models were fabricated in Kelley's Detroit model shop. With the transmission's future looking so optimistic, GM's policy committee, in consultation with GM group vice president R.K Evans and Ed Newill, decided that the Allison Division would assume the unit's continued design, development, testing, and manufacture.

After extensive testing and redesign—its concepts truly pushed available knowledge—the pioneering CD-850 matured into its first production units in Indianapolis in 1949. From inception, development and tooling were funded by Army Ordnance Department contracts.

Parallel and coincidental with the CD progress, the Detroit Transmission Division created the first Torqmatic transmission, comprising a torque converter and three-speed and reverse transmission in one unit. This pilot model, too, was intended for the medium tank but matured too late for production.

The Torqmatic found its first application in the M18 Hellcat tank destroyer. The Hellcat, equipped with a 76mm gun, was developed and produced by Buick under division general manager Harlow Curtice and chief engineer Charley Chain. The vehicle combined the Torqmatic with a Ford 650-hp engine, and was the most flexible vehicle of its kind.

First Things First

GM's primary business of making automobiles was a factor affecting the decision to transfer the Army Ordnance contracts from Detroit to Allison: Kelley and his group had to focus on what was sure to be a mushrooming car market.

Simultaneously, at Detroit Transmission, design engineer Robert M. Schaefer proposed development of the Torqmatic system for non-automotive commercial applications. Like Kelley, division manager Vic Olsen felt compelled to concentrate on auto priorities, and referred Schaefer and his Torqmatic proposals to Bob Evans.

The Torqmatic Goes to Sea

Evans was quick to support commercial applications for the new drive, and Allison again seemed the perfect place to pursue the idea. He chose marine gears as the first such project, partly because there was a ready market. A second factor was Detroit Diesel's dissatisfaction with previous gear suppliers. The Torqmatic offered an opportunity to combine marine gears and transmissions with the GM diesels in a complete line of products for commercial and pleasure boats.

John Storer, who would become chief engineer of Allison's military transmission operations, graduated from General Motors Institute in 1932 and served with Buick until 1937. He joined Allison in 1940 as a propeller drive engineer, and in 1944 began experimental work on Detroit Diesel marine gears. Storer recalls that the first marine gear was installed in a landing craft on the Detroit River and Evans spent a lot of time with the engineers there testing it. Bob Schaefer, then still at the Diesel Division, continued his liaison with Kelley's group that had devised an excellent planetary reverse gear for the marine package.

A Dilemma Is Born

The marine gear began a practice that would recurrently haunt Allison commercial transmission operations with mixed results. That practice was to proceed to volume production of a promising new product—after encouraging preliminary results—and then to struggle to refine the product after it was in the field.

On the positive side was early winning of market share to preclude significant competition. On the negative side were the prodigious costs of correcting flawed designs and manufacture as well as erosion of customer confidence. In the classic good news/bad news twist, part of the Allison mystique among long-term customers is the company's proven willingness to put things right for the customer. But profitability was often compromised in the sometimes less-than-ideal process. Three decades later the issue would become a watershed in Allison history.

Because the practice of early production has had such significance, its origins bear exploring after the precedent-setting marine gear package. Recalls John Storer:

"We went down to a shrimper at Darien, Georgia, installed the unit, and put it to work. Unfortunately, we were very successful in the first test installation. We had to do considerable development work later, and we ultimately had a successful product."

Continues Storer: "That was the way we first operated under Evans. We'd put out a product, almost without exception, leaving the design stage very early, releasing the item to production and then going through development, dynamometer work, and initial field work—really performing everything except the first round of design engineering. We had to pull more than a few rabbits out of hats.

"Bob Schaefer had been a protege of Evans, and the operating mode may have been bred into

In the early 1950s leading GM engineering executives—several of whom played major roles in the division's transmission operation—visited Allison's general manager Ed Newill (second from right). Observing a working plastic torque converter model are, from left, Robert K. Evans, C.L. McCuen, Charles F. "Boss" Kettering, Newill, and Ormand Hunt.

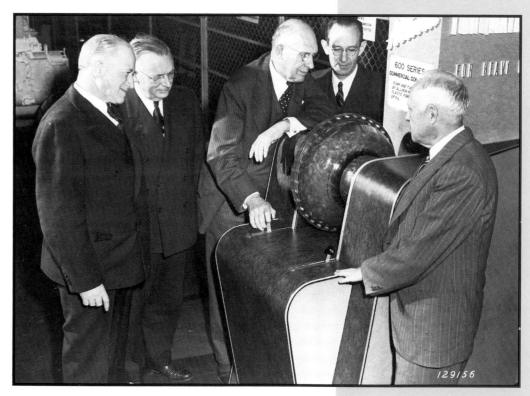

Schaefer. Eventually, it turned out to be effective, but had we spent more time and money in development, we would have saved a great deal of money in the end. But perhaps we would have given the competition an opportunity to come to Indianapolis. It's important to recognize that that's the way we lived."

Shaping Transmission Operations

Accompanying Schaefer to Allison in September 1946 was senior project engineer Hugh Kirtland. Horace Roberts was in charge of the V-drive transmission; Storer was chief engineer of ordnance transmissions; Bud Richards was chief test engineer, assisted by Frank Winchell. Johnny Lord was torque converter project engineer with Ed Sharer from Detroit Diesel and the Kelley group; Les Stoner was chief draftsman, and Howard Christenson was development engineer.

Bob Evans did not believe it practical to meld the military and commercial transmissions into the aircraft engine operations, so he persuaded Ed Newill to split the two major Allison product lines into separate units—Transmission Operations, and Aircraft [engine] Operations.

While cooperation between the groups has always been cordial and productive, the question of divisional "status" surfaced from time to time,

R.M. Schaefer, who retired as Allison's chief transmissions engineer in May 1967, is singled out with virtual unanimity by his colleagues and successors at Allison as one of the central figures in the division's founding and rise to preeminence.

A graduate of Germany's University of Munich, Bob Schaefer came to the United States in 1926 and worked for several companies as draftsman, designer, and engineer. He was vice president of the Twin Disc Company before joining GM's Detroit Transmission Division in October 1942. Soon after the start of the war, Schaefer took charge of tank transmission production at the Hydramatic Division. He was among the first senior engineering people tapped by GM group vice president Bob Evans to lead the Allison Division's entry into automatic transmissions.

At Allison, Schaefer's engineering skills and dynamic leadership style soon set the new transmission operation's tone and pace. Says one current senior manager, "Schaefer, the father of the business, was a good engineer with sheer will power and corporate contact, and an outstanding sense of people. He surrounded himself with outstanding technical talent. Schaefer was a chemist of people. We owe him the business."

Says another, "If I were to credit any one person for making this into a successful operation, it would be Bob Schaefer, by the strength of his own convictions, his strong personality. And he was also a doggone good engineer. He had sense to hire the right people, knew every single person in the whole department and what you were doing."

In the March 1989 *Journal of the Society of Automotive Engineers*, engineer Ed Mably, who left Allison in 1965 and retired from the Ford Motor Company as head of truck programs, called Schaefer "a great leader who got his people to do the job and do it right, the Vince Lombardi of the engineering world."

Although their styles differed dramatically, Schaefer shared his passionate commitment to excellence and leadership with other men who held similar roles of leadership at Allison, most notably recently-retired engineering director Mark Fisher, "the last of the transmission operation's founding giants."

even at the outset. Recalled Schaefer 43 years later, with characteristic bluntness: "Ed Newill was aircraft-minded. He spent his time with the aircraft people. We didn't get much of his time, or much of his interest."

Overall responsibility for the Transmission Engineering Department in Plant 3—and the title of transmission operations manager—went to R.E. (Bud) Lynch, who had joined Allison in 1940 (and would subsequently direct the Aeroproducts operation) as assistant to the chief engineer. Lynch, educated at the United States Military Academy at West Point, first became associated with General Motors in 1936 in the engineering department in Detroit. Lynch's staff included sales, engineering, manufacturing, inspection, and purchasing people; all except the engineers came from the aircraft engine team.

With the magnetic energy of an idea whose time has come, the transmission team swiftly became the center for projects destined to establish the industry standard in three basic application markets—heavy-duty, off-highway vehicles; on-highway vehicles heavier than passenger cars; and military tracked vehicles.

In the process, Allison became the heavy duty transmission division of General Motors. In June 1946 the Transmission Engineering Section was transferred from Plant 2 to Plant 3. A model shop was implemented, and plans were made to begin production of the marine gear for which the design had been established.

The V-drive and the Bus

Late in 1945 the GMC Truck & Coach Division had approached the parent corporation for floor space to manufacture a new V-drive transmission to replace the Spicer transmission used in transit coaches since 1938. Evans had that product, too, transferred to Allison, where studies for its manufacture continued and tooling was soon begun.

Another Product Study Group effort was a new type of inter-city bus transmission, also in collaboration with Truck & Coach, and aimed at Greyhound.

The first V-drive hydraulic transmission for GMC Truck & Coach Division's transit buses was prepared for testing at Allison's Plant 4 in October 1947 by, from left, E.F. Miller, Frank Woodlock, Lloyd Starnes, Vic Eichburg, and Henry Bruder. The last V transmission, number 65,389, was built in July 1976.

In production for more than a decade after its introduction in 1948 as the first buses with Allison's V-drive, GMC Truck & Coach TDH Series coaches dominated U.S. municipal bus transit. This TDH-5106 unit was built in 1957.

Because the V design seemed more suitable than the original concept, that project was turned over to Allison in June 1946, but was overtaken by torque converter technology in 1947. It never reached production.

The V-drive (so named because of the acute angle of intersection between engine and transmission required by the cramped space at the rear of the typical city bus) began as a single-speed, forward automatic, converter drive with an automatic lockup shift done off the flywheel. The early drive's central problem was how to engage two splines rotating at different speeds, and the solution was the bullet-nosed spline that gave the units their characteristic "crisp" shifts. The first production units were delivered in October 1947.

As with every commercial automatic transmission, the V-drive possessed inherent virtues that justified its additional initial cost in comparison with the manual transmission it supplanted. For bus operators, in addition to its other advantages, the drive's basic appeal was salary savings. Recalls Schaefer, "The extra cost of a torque converter for the Fifth Avenue bus in New York, for instance, was justified because the driver, freed from gear-shifting tasks, could perform the duties previously handled by the conductor. So a job was eliminated." The V-drive reached full production late in 1948 with an order for some 900 coaches for the City of New York.

The next major V-drive refinement came in 1955, a two-speed unit with a range shift, the VS-2, built in two versions. One ran with the 6V-71 engine, the other for the 8V-71 fitted to the handsome, classic GM buses. Almost every year improvements were made to the V-line transmissions as Allison and GMC T&C engineers pursued lower sound levels, smoother shifts, durability, and low cost. In 1958 the VH unit was introduced with hydraulic and direct clutches.

In 1975 Allison introduced an off-shoot of the new automatic line—the AT/MT/HT—into the V-drive. The VS-2 was replaced with the V 730, a three-speed modern automatic in the same configuration as the two-range VS-2 for the same types of buses. In 1983 electronic controls were introduced to that transmission, the V 731. In 1990 an output retarder was added and the designation changed to the VR 730—the division's V-drive until replaced by a still more efficient adaptation of the forthcoming World Transmission.

"The Other Products"

As the division developed its transmission expertise, much of the huge Speedway and Maywood residual production capacity from WWII was also being turned to good use—use that not only brought in revenue but expanded Allison's resources and reputation.

Whether helping Delco to meet the GM auto plants' voracious demand for shock absorbers or the Electro-Motive Division to dieselize the nation's railways, Allison proved that its manufacturing resources were as dynamic as its engineering was creative.

Sid Smock, who retired as division manufacturing manager in 1984 after 34 Allison years, reflected on the value of the so-called ancillary production that burgeoned after 1946: "We took the shock absorber job to help meet the demand as Delco was switching to the new cylindrical shocks while we produced the old kind. Our women workers in particular had the dexterity to handle this sort of volume. We worked it

Among components built at Indianapolis for EMD locomotives were alternator coils that helped to generate electricity for main traction motors and accessories. Seven hundred feet of wire in 144 individual coils are wrapped with nearly 1,000 yards of tape to protect against dust and moisture.

A staple of Allison manufacture from its earliest days, Roots-type blowers continued their significance for contemporary diesel engines in these alloy cases and lobes manufactured for the diesel-electric railway locomotives of GMs Electro-Motive Division.

so we could handle 14,000 units per eight-hour shift, a great learning job for Allison.

"Our work with locomotive components for EMD in La Grange was even more remarkable. They were building two locomotives per day, and our content rose to more than 10 tons per locomotive, about 12 percent—traction gears, axle gears, pinions, generators, alternators, stators, pumps and pump gears, valve bridges, rocker arms, blowers. The work was surely among the finest manufacturing Allison ever did, and marked by camaraderie and efficiency. Our pinion gears and traction gears, all precision ground, were the best in the world. We had gears go a million miles with no visible wear. In the bearing plant, we had slipper rods and main and connecting rod bearings with a million miles and the lead still on them."

Going Off-Road

Allison's first foray into the off-highway business came with Allis-Chalmers of Springfield, Ohio, after considerable on-site persuasion from Schaefer and Kirtland. Early in 1947 Allis-Chalmers asked GM to develop a new powershift transmission for their HD-9 Tractor. Twin Disc's torque converter had been in use, but Allis-Chalmers felt the tractor performance could be improved if a powershift unit was developed with the converter. The concept was developed during 1946-47. Test models were built, but the project did not reach production.

Nonetheless, the episode provided the basis for projects with the Euclid Road Machinery Company of Euclid, Ohio. Allison's first Euclid experiment was on a bottom dumper. The immediate advantage was that power could be transmitted to both front and rear of the vehicle, allowing greater job site flexibility and control. The installation was the first with twin power. Detroit Diesel engines were matched to an Allison torque converter and transmission in the tractor and the same kind of unit at the rear end of the dumper.

In this project, and many to follow, the Torqmatic principle gave off-road vehicles such a productivity boost that other manufacturers soon explored the idea for themselves. Allison continued to make Torqmatics for shovels, front end loaders, road rollers, and graders. Almost all used either torque converter or torque converter and transmission. Later, separate units were abandoned in favor of combined units, reducing installation problems.

Euclid's need for a transmission for a proposed 40-ton diesel-powered truck led to a 200-hp series of converters, and the TC-900 Series converter went into production in September 1948 for twin Detroit Diesel units for oil field use.

A major breakthrough came with construction of facilities that could duplicate field conditions on a test stand. Previously, engineers had been confined to testing gears one at a time and were unable to test clutches moving in transition from one load situation to another. Now, they went into the field and gathered computer data on work-site performance, then transferred the data into the test equipment—a big Allison first. People from Caterpillar and International Harvester came to look at the program, and it was copied repeatedly.

The new technology continued to impress its users. Bob Schaefer recalled that when Torqmatic transmissions for rear-dump trucks were evaluated, an Allison team went to the Phoenix Proving Grounds where International Harvester was testing trucks with and without Torqmatics. At lunchtime Schaefer asked the evaluators if they'd found any advantage,

Among the earliest off-highway applications for the new Torqmatic technology were the Euclid Road Machinery Company's ground-breaking double-engine bottom dumpers and scrapers. With its paired Torqmatic converters and TG transmissions, this bottom scraper of 1948 was powered with Detroit Diesel engines.

As part of America's post-WWII railroad renaissance, the 85-foot-long, lightweight Budd Rail Diesel Car promised appealing and economical advantages for certain light-traffic and commuter railroad routes. Twin Detroit Diesel 275-hp 6-110 engines mated to Allison Torqmatic transmissions were mounted beneath the car.

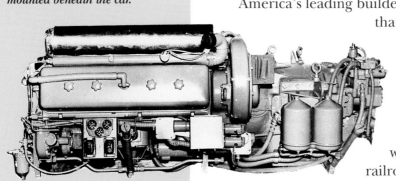

The Rail Car (RC) transmission comprised a heavy-duty torque converter and single-speed forward and reverse gearing, with lockup to direct drive at 55 mph, to allow smooth acceleration and a top speed of 83 mph. A total of 1,432 units were made from 1949 to 1964.

and one said: "Look at the shirts of the two drivers. The driver with the stick-shift truck is wet all over his back; the other guy's shirt is absolutely clean."

The torque converter permitted the limited-power diesel engine to be used as a full-range power device. In tandem with the diesel engine, the converter replicated characteristics of a series-wound electric motor to provide similar power results.

In June 1948 Allison introduced the first torque converter-power shift transmission combination to commercial operators of off-highway equipment: the Torqmatic Converter and TG-Series transmission team quickly proved their superiority in mining trucks, oil field operations, and earth movers.

The Rail Diesel Car, RDC-1

Detroit Diesel had developed a new six-cylinder engine, the 6-110, to produce 300 hp. In 1947 the Budd Company of Philadelphia, one of America's leading builders of railway cars, proposed a commuter-type car that would be self-propelled with diesel engines underneath.

At the request of Detroit Diesel, Allison visited Budd and began a project to develop a single-speed tailored transmission to be used with twin pairs of 6-110 engines in each car. Test models, capable of more than 83 mph top speed, were received with enthusiasm by several railroads. The railcar transmission, the Model RC, went into production in December 1949 for both domestic and overseas use, but not without some awkward moments.

The most demanding difficulty was inadequate performance of the electric solenoids incorporated as part of the transmission shifting system. Hugh Kirtland, then chief commercial products engineer, recalled the difficulty: "The rail cars required only one man to control dual-cab operation. When the units were coupled together as trains, say from Camden to Atlantic City, the

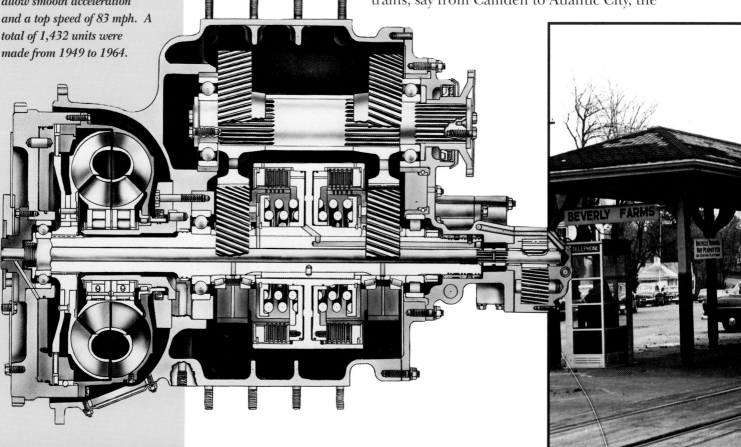

solenoids would malfunction and one engine would not shift. The result was basket-case engines. We'd started with Delco automotive solenoids, but they were simply not strong enough. Truck solenoids were a little better, but finally we designed a kind of latch-plate lock for the solenoids before they could shift."

The rail car had looked promising as a replacement for the old interurban railways and the commuter market. Changing patterns in U.S. intercity travel, however, accelerated by improved highways, limited sales of the sleek cars to only a few areas. Egypt was a significant purchaser, and several cars went in to service in Australia. By 1953, 277 units had been delivered. Four model variants were built, concluding with 1964's RC-4, incorporating TC-500 elements, for use in Brazil. Production totalled 1,432 units and ended in 1965.

Mark Fisher, who retired as ATD engineering director in 1990, began his career at Allison in 1947 following graduation from Purdue. As a senior project engineer in 1961, he devoted more than a few hours to design of the control mechanism for the TT 2000 Series transmissions.

The Secret Automatic

The division had a brief courtship with passenger car transmissions, the Allison AA transmission. It used a converter with lockup and gears—developed for Pontiac, Oldsmobile, Chevrolet, and Buick. The converter and lockup was a forerunner of the mechanism now used in all automatic transmissions for fuel economy. Mark Fisher recalls the episode:

"I came in February 1947 as a mechanical engineer directly from Purdue University and began in torque converter design and worked in various hydraulic programs in the early years. In 1949-1950, we began work on a passenger car transmission, a project not very well known because we never actually got into production. But we worked on it for about three years.

"We had the Allison Automatic Passenger Car Transmission [projected for] all GM cars here in the states, and GM of Canada cars, and Opel and

Among the RDC's largest fleets was that of the Boston and Maine, which used their more than 60 cars singly and in trains up to the maximum of 11 cars. In the U.S. and overseas, RDCs proved durable and efficient, with per-mile costs less than half of comparable steam power operations.

some jeeps. We were really going for that business. The motivation for
the project was that some of our early people, including Howard
Christenson, came from Hydramatic—then building the passenger car
transmissions, of course—and they were still interested in some of that
work. The project was treated with some secrecy, called the AAT tractor
transmission so that nobody would know what it was, complete with an
iron curtain in the back of the plant. We made perhaps 45 units, and it
was released at Pontiac in about 1951. But they had the fire at the
Livonia Hydramatic plant about that time, and GM decided that they
couldn't have duplication of efforts."

Refining a Winner

Progress continued on the military projects as well, including final
development work on the CD-850 transmission. By February 1947 the
first CD-850-1 had been produced in Allison's aircraft engine model shop,
and 17 pilots delivered by September. The transmission was planned,
under great pressure from the military, for immediate production, only a
year after the project had been transferred to Indianapolis.

Fortunately, the vehicle project was delayed and Allison was able to
finish the transmission development before the first application. The
first installations were only to be some hundred odd, built by conversion
of the Pershing tank. As described by John Storer, "We cut the M26
Pershing's bustle off and reshaped it around the CD-850 transmission and
we began to test in earnest at the Detroit Arsenal, at Kentucky's Fort
Knox, and at Aberdeen Proving Ground in Maryland."

Colonel Cummins' Cutoff

One critical problem lay in the original CD-850 steer system that was engaged by freewheel directly to the engine. Effectively, it was designed so that the tank would slow in the same ratio as the engine: the slower the tank speed, the tighter the turn would be. When the engine came to stall, the tank would pivot turn.

John Storer described the resulting phenomenon: "When a driver approached a turn, especially downhill, he'd hit the clutch for the turn, feeling that he had lots of steer. Then in the turn he'd put on full steer. But as the engine speed dropped, his ability to continue steering diminished in proportion, and soon he'd practically lose all steer.

"At Fort Knox, there was a winding, steep downhill road with a sharp drop off. It took a lot of guts on the part of the driver, who wanted to slow down on those curves, to put his foot into full throttle if he was going to make the turn.

"We had a Col. Cummins down there who said, 'I can do that.' Forever after, the spot was known as Col. Cummins Cutoff, when his tank took off through the trees."

Refining the CD-850

Two field-generated design changes extended the CD-850's life, observed retired chief applications engineer Dale Hasler, and made it the most widely used transmission in

The 30-mile Munson Test Course at Aberdeen Proving Ground, near Baltimore, Maryland, as a primary Army vehicle test site has hosted many of the vehicles in which Allison transmissions have become standard equipment. The facility is run by the U.S. Army Combat Systems Test Activity (USACSTA) under the Test and Evaluation Command (TECOM) of the Army Materiel Command (AMC).

For many members of Allison's military transmission team, during more than four decades the garages and hilly roads of Fort Knox, Kentucky, have been almost as much a workplace as the Indianapolis plants. The Army's "Home of Cavalry & Armor," Fort Knox is a major tracked and wheeled vehicle test site.

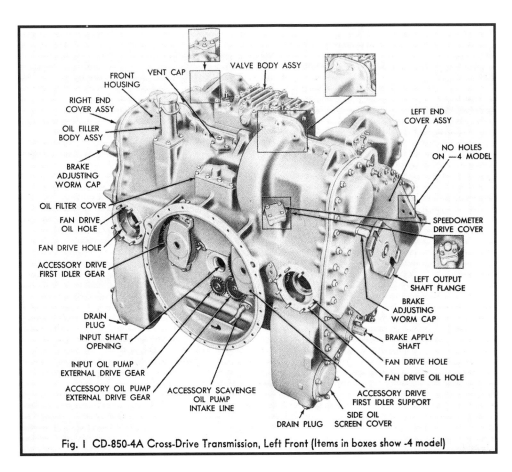

Fig. 1 CD-850-4A Cross-Drive Transmission, Left Front (Items in boxes show -4 model)

Facing page: While this bit of road is actually at GM's Military Proving Ground near Milford, Michigan, it matches John Storer's description of the notorious Col. Cummins' Cutoff at Fort Knox. The jeep, testing an Allison AAJ transmission in the early 1950s, presumably negotiated the curve uneventfully.

Accompanying every production transmission is a set of service and maintenance manuals. Allison support documents have earned high praise from both commercial and military users for their clarity and utility, typified by this page from the 1952 **Drivers/Mechanics Handbook: CD-850 Transmission.**

any tracked vehicle in the world. "The first was the change to output-driven steering. The reason was that Frank Blair knew about it: he was a tanker in WWII's M4 Sherman tanks. They had a control differential that was basically output driven. If you move, you have to steer regardless of what the engine is doing. That change is attributable to Frank Blair and John Storer. Blair, in his 1949 General Motors Institute thesis, showed how to do it; and his study of tracked vehicles became the bible used by the Army for years.

"Second, we made the transmission more efficient. With early CD-850s, vehicle performance suffered because of the high losses in the transmission. While the torque converter has an inherent loss in it, the problem went beyond that. You don't shift a range of gears, just use the converter with the CD-850's four-to-one torque multiplication. Further, we had brakes: at 30 mph, those brakes absorb 100 horsepower out of the 650 you start with. And the steer clutches, even when not steering, were churning oil.

Dale Hasler, who joined Allison in 1940, served as chief military applications engineer during much of Allison's formative time with the U.S. Army. He participated in every aspect of the division's military transmission programs until his retirement in 1982.

"In one change, we retrieved about 40 hp simply by ventilating the steer clutch to get rid of the oil. We worked on the brakes and took out three oil pumps: we even had a scavenge pump in the front that scavenged the oil that spilled between the engine and the transmission. We put a scoop in there that let the flywheel kick the oil out.

"By changing the steering in 1950 and improving the efficiency in 1951 when we went from the Dash 3 to Dash 4, we made the CD-850 our bread-and-butter for years. Even with its converter without a lockup, the CD-850 was more efficient than the M1 tank's X-1100 of 1979 with its lockup clutch and four-speed transmission."

The first production CD-850 was delivered on September 30, 1949, just four months after manufacturing machinery was installed in Plant 3. By June 1952 10,000 were in service, and peak volume of 4,254 units was reached in 1953. By 1987 more than 44,000 had been delivered for service in more than a dozen heavy tracked military vehicle types, including those of Britain, Israel, Spain, and Sweden.

Production of the CD-850 transmission started in 1950 for the M46 Patton medium tank that was derived from the M26 Pershing. During the next 10 years, the U.S. Army's main battle tank progressed to the M47, through three versions of the M48 and finally to the diesel-powered M60, still in production in 1989. In addition to the prime application in medium tanks, substantial numbers of other vehicles used the CD-850 including the M53 and M55 self-propelled artillery, and the M103 heavy tank.

But the CD-850 stayed the same—efficient, simple, reliable and, with sustained production, sufficiently economical that Allison sold it overseas, to Britain, Israel, and Spain.

The CD's First War

The contract on the first 1,000 CD-850 transmissions was near completion when the

Korean Conflict began. The CD-850-equipped Patton tank was performing well when Allison received a contract to build the CD-500 transmission for the M41 Walker Bulldog light tank. The division was required to simultaneously increase CD-850 production fourfold and begin producing the CD-500. People had to be reassigned, many new ones hired and trained. New machines had to be purchased, old ones reworked.

Manufacture of the Bulldog sparked another volume of GM legends beginning with the assignment of Cadillac division general manager Ed Cole to manage the high-priority project. The light tank prototype was designed, with the CD-500 transmission, and a production location was

Among rigorous Army tank tests is deep water fording. Fitted with intake and exhaust extensions, at full throttle the 45-ton M46 generated a two-foot bow wave while being put through its paces along a Michigan lakefront in June 1950.

The first of the General Patton series of medium tanks, the M46 built by Chrysler's Detroit Tank Arsenal, was the principal U.S. tank in Korea and established the battlefield credentials of Allison's CD-850 crossdrive transmission.

In one of the corporation's most productive careers, before serving as GM's president from 1967 to 1974, Edward N. Cole made important contributions at Chevrolet and Cadillac. His energetic management of the M41 Walker tank project in Cleveland in the early 1950s was a model of its kind.

Designed for reconnaissance, operation over rough terrain, and even airborne delivery, the 27-ton M41 Walker Bulldog light tank used

Allison's CD-500 transmission and was built by GM's Cadillac division at the Cleveland Army Tank & Automotive Plant.

needed. The Ordnance Department, noting that Chrysler had a tank plant (the Detroit Arsenal plant) and Ford had an engine plant, asked Cadillac to take on the Cleveland facility that had built tanks earlier and was then a storage facility. Cole, who had previously managed the plant, was assigned to bring Cleveland on line.

The Fabled Beans

Under Cole's direction, Cadillac took over the Cleveland Army Tank Automotive Plant, and 20 GM divisions provided staffing. At the time, the plant—built by GM in WWII to produce the Allison V-3420-powered Boeing B-39 bomber that never saw production— was a warehouse for surplus goods and confiscated German equipment.

In eight months Cadillac removed 349 railway carloads of material from the plant (including 24 million pounds of beans), installed more than 4,000 machines in preparation for vehicle production, and produced the first M41 tank three months ahead of schedule in April 1951. By 1958 Cadillac had produced nearly 6,000 M41 light tanks and M42 anti-aircraft vehicles fitted with Allison CD-500 powertrains.

The Cleveland plant, which hosted extensive tank design, engineering, and production for the Army from 1950 to 1975, would play a role in Allison's subsequent history, as well.

Yet Another Speedy Launch

Allison was required to produce the CD-500 to match production of the Bulldog. So swift was Detroit's decision-making that even Ed Newill learned about his division's role nearly after the fact. John Storer smiled broadly as he remembered the occasion:

"Bob Evans came down to tell us what to do to match Ed Cole's production moves on the Walker tank. Ed Newill sat in the meeting next to Cy Osborn, who was our vice president (next in the organization chart between Newill and Evans, who was executive vice president). Evans spoke of how soon we were going to be building, and Newill stood up to say that we couldn't do that. Osborn grabbed him by the coattails to sit down.

"Evans was not only saying what we had to do, but had a plan to do it. The plan was that we weren't going to tool it all up, but we'd do the transmission case and some principal parts. The rest we were going to farm out around the country and into the divisions until it was essentially a model shop production from wherever we could find someone to make the parts for us.

"And Ed Newill was first learning about it at this meeting. And it worked. We got into production. However, as usual, development was far from complete. We had installations of our first production units and began to encounter our failures—at the tank plant. [The problem was traced to vibration fatigue in key bolts.] Ed Cole began to get cold feet, so he asked Oliver Kelley to build him a less sophisticated iron case transmission because the CD-500 had been required by the military to be as light as we could design it.

"Fortunately, tank build-up was just beginning, and they were not yet building many tanks. We were ahead of them in quantity but going through difficulty with these failures. Cole went back to Kelley: 'Give me a transmission quickly which I might use if Allison doesn't come through and get this CD-500 operating in our tanks.' Kelley's ability was to crash something like that, which he did. In three months he had a transmission to play with.

"Meanwhile, we had re-engineered the problem bolts and put the threads entirely in the mating part, instead of partially in and partially out, eliminating a sharp recess that had allowed vibration to fatigue the bolt. With things like that, pulling rabbits out of the hat, we got more reliability out of that transmission than we had in the 850. It was beautiful, quite an experience, under the pressures we had. I stuck my neck out, and lucked out."

By July 1951 Cadillac's M41 production line was in full swing, followed close behind in Indianapolis at the new Plant 7. Early Cadillac production schedules were seemingly impossibly short, but Allison managed to deliver the first CD-500s four months early, and had shipped its first 500 units to Cleveland within 53 weeks of being authorized for production.

In eight years, almost 6,000 M41s and M42 anti-aircraft vehicles were built. At GM's 50th Anniversary Chicago Powerama Exhibition in 1955, the two vehicles were featured in a simulated field maintenance demonstration. The combined engine and CD-500 transmission unit is suspended by mobile crane over the M42 hull.

The Old Plant Trick

For CD-500 production a long-deserted Chrysler warehouse on Northwestern Avenue in Indianapolis was procured. The concrete floors were neither strong enough nor in good enough repair to support production machinery; neither were powerhouse steam, compressed air, or hot water matched to the need. So upgrading work began immediately on the building, designated Plant 7.

Putting new plants on line was by then an Allison specialty. The first production part was run exactly three months after verbal authorization was received to begin the construction work, and the majority of the Plant 7 reconstruction was completed within nine months.

The CD-500 production release came on September 8, 1950, and the first units were available five months later.

Division Reorganization

The intensified production for the Korean War prompted changes in the Allison management structure. In February 1951 the division was reorganized into four separate entities—Aircraft Operations, Transmission Operations, Bearing Operations, and Locomotive Parts Operations. Financial and personnel served all four operations; otherwise, each had their separate staff.

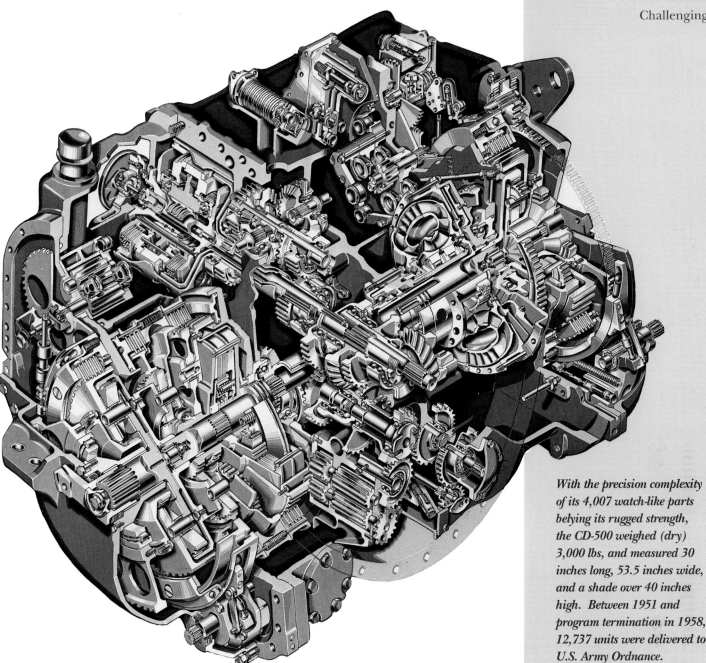

With the precision complexity of its 4,007 watch-like parts belying its rugged strength, the CD-500 weighed (dry) 3,000 lbs, and measured 30 inches long, 53.5 inches wide, and a shade over 40 inches high. Between 1951 and program termination in 1958, 12,737 units were delivered to U.S. Army Ordnance.

Some Inherited Limits

On the commercial side of Transmission Operations, technical thickets were not the only difficulty managers encountered as Allison made its uncharted way in a new industry. Some problems arose from the nature of the company and its role with its parent corporation and its companion enterprise at Allison, the aircraft engine operation.

Bob Schaefer sketched the context: "Needless to say, these products suffered from a top-heavy organization and the burden rates were much higher than was the practice of other commercial transmission builders. Further, manufacturing was saddled with an organization with an aircraft and 'cost plus' background. This did not help us compete in the market used to products from Spicer, Clark, Fuller, and others. But the thing that controlled our progress most was the trouble that we were having with each new product. After all, we were pioneering and attempting to go down a road where nobody had gone before."

Why Does a Division Cross the Road?

Having secured two important market niches, the Transmission Operations team was about to pave the way to a challenging future down the road, in a manner of speaking. And their first vehicle, suitably enough, would be a friendly Chevrolet truck.

CHAPTER 8

Evolving

Crossdrives and Customer Service.
Off-highway inroads: retarders,
vocations, setting standards.
Converting torque efficiently.
Cracking the Third Niche: the Chevrolet
CPT-4 and the MT.
Creating a Market: Selling the end
user; the demonstration;
the Ultimate Vocation.
Vietnam and Cleveland.
Ed Newill Retires.
Consolidating the AT-MT-HT Family.

Previous page: As vehicle manufacturers "grew" off-highway trucks for greater efficiency, Allison transmissions kept pace. For this mammoth KW-Dart Series D2551 dump truck, the CLBT 6061 introduced in 1963 was ideal. It accommodated engines in the 600-hp power range.

T he Korean Conflict had not only proved Allison's responsiveness to national emergency yet again. In its duration from June 1950 to July 1953, the war also established the division as the U.S. Army's prime supplier of transmissions for tracklaying vehicles, a position not seriously challenged since.

The Customer Service Foundation

Fittingly, the military operations that began Allison's commitment to vehicular transmission development were soon functionally organized to focus on customer needs. That focus had been included in Jim Allison's directives to his staff at the beginning of WWI, and it would continue to serve the company well. But its concrete implementation in the burgeoning military business was exemplary.

In autumn 1954 the transmission engineering department, under Bob Schaefer, was reorganized. Notes Dale Hasler, "The applications department was designated as a separate function. Previously the product engineer was responsible for an application and installation. Now, the department's sole responsibility was to work with the customer, to see that he got what he wanted and that we got what we needed.

"We didn't have a military sales department, we had a contract department. Basically we did the military sales and Harold Fulton and

Ralph Forbes from the contracts department travelled with us. We'd write up the scope of work and they would put it into contract language. That's how sales were made.

"A key to our successful military transmission business came with the separate applications department," continued Hasler. "The department prepared the specifications for a transmission: we talked to the government and made performance studies to determine what they needed. We wrote the specs, then turned them over to product people to design and develop. We were involved in testing in the field, working with the vehicle designer, beginning with the government people, then the vehicle contractor. Because the applications department represented the customer, we would fight for the customer. Bob Schaefer used to say, 'I'll be pushing you out, but keep your foot in the door, don't let me close that door.'"

Hugh Kirtland was the first chief applications engineer, and there were two applications supervisors, Paul Bonham for commercial projects, Hasler for the military. Basically, the transmission operations' institutional emphasis on customers started in 1954. Frank Blair was chief military engineer.

The Retarder and Off-Highway Growth

As the CD swiftly won its place on the battlefield (by February 1954 the 30,000th transmission was delivered to the military), the Torqmatic transmission continued to prove its superiority in off-highway commercial uses, particularly as Allison engineers worked closely with vehicle makers to adapt the technology to field-defined needs. Among touchstone improvements was the addition of retarder capability to the transmission to powerfully supplement conventional vehicle braking.

Work on the retarder was begun in 1951 at the request of the Euclid Company, whose scrapers in the Philippines were operating on grades so steep that wheel brakes were almost completely ineffective. A retarder, not unlike a paddle wheel in an oil bath, employs a varied rotor between stator vanes in a retarder housing, to use the transmission's fluid to provide hydrodynamic retardation to help control vehicle downhill speed.

Retarder braking is obtained when transmission oil is directed (by the operator) into the retarder housing. The oil causes a resistance to rotation of the varied rotor which is transferred to the rotor shaft. This retardation power is transmitted through the transmission to the drivetrain and the vehicle's driving wheels, which slow the vehicle.

By the mid-1980s, retarders were combined with the Allison Transmission Electronic Control (ATEC) on some transmissions to provide the most precise possible transmission operation. Both retarder types are capable of generating braking capacity in the 500-hp range in Allison's HT 700 and MT 600 series on-highway units, and up to 2,000 hp in some hauling transmissions.

Because the retarder absorbs total engine horsepower, or more, a good deal of heat dissipation is required. Cooling is accomplished by using the retarding pump characteristic: huge amounts of oil—200 gallons per minute—can be pumped through a heat exchange unit, typically an oil-to-water heat exchanger using the vehicle radiator system.

The retarder was particularly welcome for the huge (50-ton and greater) mine haul trucks that routinely scale and descend steep grades. In the vast, gaping vermilion pits of Minnesota's Mesabi Range, from which much of the nation's iron ore was long mined, more than 1,400 Allison retarder-equipped transmissions were in service by 1965.

Serving as Transmission Operations first commercial applications supervisor was Paul Bonham. Dale Hasler served as his military applications counterpart.

Facing page: Abandoning their drawing boards for a moment on April 26, 1952, were some of the men who constructed the Allison Transmission foundations. From left, Oscar Stevens, Ford Lyons, Les Stoner, Bob Schaefer, Howard Christenson, Ed Sharer, John Storer, Hugh Kirtland, Frank Blair, Bernie Hartz, and Dick Anderson.

In 1952, when the division had delivered its 10,000th transmission, the first retarder, mounted between the converter and the transmission, was tested. Production units, called the Torqmatic brake, began coming off the line in February 1953, and variations of the device have been offered on almost every off-highway transmission developed since.

Expanding "Vocations"

The decade brought discovery to both Allison and new customers for whose work the torque converter and the automatic offered important advantages over manual gearboxes. New applications (among Allison engineers, the more elegant "vocations" is often heard) were added steadily.

Typical was the road-paving industry. A pavement roller must reverse direction without roll, slippage, or swell at the end of each pass. With mechanical transmissions, rollers had to be over-powered because drivers didn't have time for shifting gears other than reverse. Drivers routinely slipped the clutch to avoid the abrupt engagement of engine power that spoiled newly-laid blacktop.

The TC-200 and -300 series converters for engines from 40 to 150 hp provided the torque management required for smooth reversing, making the larger roller unnecessary and greatly reducing driver load. A three-speed forward, three-speed reverse transmission with a "sense-feel" reversing valve that slipped the clutches for soft engagement allowed the operator to change directly from second gear forward to second gear reverse.

During 1953 the Michigan Division of Clark Equipment Co. introduced a line of front-end loaders with full powershift transmissions, an industry

Below and facing page: Introduced in 1973, the CLBT 750 automatic has five forward ranges and integral retarder for downhill speed control and accommodates engine power between 250 to 400 hp. It is fitted here to a 28-yard Terex 33-05 end dump truck operated by Johnson Brothers Highway and Heavy Constructors for a highway building job near Hibbing, Minnesota, on the Mesabi Range.

first. The installation offered convincing proof to the loader industry that the powershift was the answer to their problems and began a minor revolution. In order to compete, eight front-end loader manufacturers approached Allison in August 1954 and agreed to a crash program for development of a front-end loader transmission to be in production by the following summer.

Euclid Joins the GM Family

When GM acquired the Euclid Road Machinery Company in 1953 (the unit became the Euclid Division), plans were made to expand production from trucks and scrapers into a full construction equipment line—crawler tractors, loaders, graders and trucks in several sizes. Allison was asked to develop a transmission for their tractors, the CRT-5530 that was introduced in September 1954. In 1956, due to the success of their 18- and 24-yard twin engine scrapers, Euclid offered a 12-yard scraper incorporating the twin-engine layout and planned a powershift transmission for the single-engine seven-yard scraper. Accordingly, in April 1957 Allison introduced the CT-3340 transmission.

International Harvester in 1954 chose to add trucks and scrapers to their line of construction crawler tractors. To provide transmissions for the new lines, Allison started with a clean slate and developed what became the CLBT-5640 transmission, a four-speed torque converter unit with the Torqmatic retarder and all the features then identified as useful in the off-highway environment. The transmission was introduced in the International Harvester Model 95 off-highway truck in May 1956.

Transmission Nomenclature

The basic off-highway transmission designations were applied early: CT for the converter-transmission package; CLT for the package with a lockup clutch; CL(B)T with the hydraulic retarder; and DP, designating a dual path transmission with lockup clutch and hydraulic retarder. The CRT designation covers the powershift transmissions for cycling applications—compactors, material handling units, shovel loaders, and similar uses. The TC designation alone denotes the torque converter.

The Occasional Curiosity

In 1955 the Army negotiated a development program with the FWD Corporation of Clintonville, Wisconsin, for a vehicle that would be able to traverse the frozen Arctic wastes. The proposal was to use Rolligon bags in place of tires, which would permit the vehicle to negotiate any type of terrain. The original concept used an experimental Allison transmission, the TX-340, an early version of a proposed middle-size, off-highway transmission that eventually became the CLBT-4460.

Torque Converter Design

Central to every Allison automatic transmission installation is a torque converter, and improvements in the performance and economy of this vital component have been the special province of master torque converter design engineer Harry Fackenthal since he arrived at Allison in October 1955.

Then Allison was trying to get away from the four element converter—units with two stators—but had not yet developed a satisfactory three-element converter, certain to lower costs and raise efficiency. Fackenthal's first major task was to convert all of Allison's units from four-element converters to three.

Says Fackenthal, "You're always looking for more capacity in a torque converter, to accommodate a bigger engine without making the converter bigger. The three-element instead of four-element converter gave an immediate leap in capacity of about 300 rpm."

Notes retired engineer Leon Onken, who worked with Fackenthal for many years, "We tried to devise ways to reduce manufacturing cost and still maintain performance. When Harry came, we concentrated on better methods of production. He found that he could increase capacity by actually using a smaller diameter converter with blade geometry changes and getting improved capacity without sacrificing torque ratio or performance."

Among major cost saving changes were improved blade and vane designs, especially those that used integral casting in place of component buildup. Observes Fackenthal, "A converter normally uses 29 different blades in the pump element. If, instead of making 29 cores by hand and setting them in the ring you can design a corebox that has all the vanes in it and just pour the solid ring, you've saved 25 percent in pump elements."

Leon Onken recalls, "I accused Fackenthal of using black magic on his design of the torque converter. I think

Leon Onken began at Allison in 1944 and retired as chief draftsman for transmission engineering in 1986.

he did things by eyeball rather than science—trial and error—except he has done a lot of it and they were all good. He could design a contour, or whatever, and the thing would do what he said it would do. But try to ask him to explain it!"

"They laugh at my trial and error methods," replies Fackenthal, "but sometimes it's the only way to get there because you have no other options but to make that idea work. It may not work the first time, but chances are, after two or three whacks, you're going to make it work."

The Chevrolet and the Third Niche

Early emphasis in powershift development had been keyed to the needs of the off-highway users. But for the on-highway operator, the only modern transmissions available were "beefed-up" passenger car units. In January 1953 the Chevrolet Division was ready to explore an automatic transmission for their ton-and-a-half and two-ton trucks.

The GM corporate executive committee met at Allison and assigned the division the task of getting an automatic truck transmission into production as quickly as possible. Simultaneously, the committee directed Allison to abandon its passenger car transmission work altogether.

Bob Schaefer recalls, "The Chevrolet truck transmission was first developed as a powershift, to be manually shifted through the four gears. We took it to the GM Proving Grounds, where Chevrolet's chief engineer Ed Cole said, 'If you're going to spend all that money to tool up that transmission, why don't you make it an automatic?'"

Design engineer Harry Fackenthal joined Allison in 1955 and has been the operation's torque converter wizard even past his nominal retirement in 1989.

Allison's Own Museum

On February 9-10, 1954, Allison opened the Powerama Museum on the main floor of Plant 3. Handsomely laid out and incorporating state-of-the art museum design and imaginative lighting, the spacious exhibition included current Allison products, displays tracing the company's historical development, and lots of gleaming cutaway and working models.

Overhead hovered an armada of builders models of 51 aircraft types that Allison engines had powered from 1937. On polished oak stood a Patton tank that could be driven in place to demonstrate the wonders of its crossdrive transmission. Everywhere were photomurals, models of trucks and buses and locomotives, diagrams, dioramas, real engines and transmissions.

Taking advantage of the opening day gathering of VIPs and the press, Ed Newill made ceremonial presentations to the USAF and the Army Ordnance Corps of Allison's 30,000th military transmission and its 25,000th jet engine.

A constant source of pride to employees, the Powerama was open to the public and attracted as many as 80,000 visitors each year. The aircraft displays were dismantled in 1984 and moved to Plant 8 as the Powerama gave way to needed office space. Recently the materials were reorganized to focus on transmissions, with a special display honoring founder Jim Allison.

The Powerama offered effective and popular teaching tools, providing technical and historical data. In February 1970, sixth graders from Martinsville's East School paused on their tour to learn about a heavy-duty powershift transmission, accompanied by their teachers, James Boardman (left), and Kenneth Addington.

As it came off the line in January 1956, the first CPT-4 Powermatic transmission, scheduled for a Chevrolet truck as Allison's inauguration into the on-highway market, was duly shared with general manager Ed Newill by transmissions operations manager Kenneth Hoffman.

Cole's advice led to a fully automatic truck transmission that combined torque converter, retarder, and automatic transmission with provisions for lockup into direct drive. This first automatic transmission designed specifically for highway trucks began production in January 1956, and assembly of trucks with the Powermatic transmission began in February. The press announcement of Allison's inaugural foray onto America's highways read:

"Designed and developed by Allison in cooperation with the Chevrolet Motor Division, the transmission is the CPT-4 Powermatic, scheduled for service in a new line of Chevrolet trucks," general manager Ed Newill said, "and is a logical extension for highway use of the Allison Torqmatic drive now in widespread use in off-highway equipment nationwide and abroad."

He continued, "We are entering the on-highway truck line for the first time with the aim of providing the highway truck operator with the ease of handling that we have provided for the off-highway operator in the production of more than 75,000 Torqmatic drives for military and industrial use."

Chevrolet held an "exclusive" for the first year, but was soon followed by the competition. Henry Ford II called Harlow Curtice and said Ford didn't choose to spend the money to develop an automatic transmission for their trucks. Could Ford buy his transmission from GM? The following year, Ford adapted the Allison unit to its line as the Transmatic and thereafter became a long-time Allison transmission customer.

In 1958 Reo, Dodge, and General Motors Truck & Coach listed the transmission as an option in their heavy-duty lines. Diamond-T followed in 1959; White and International Harvester joined the swing in 1961, the same year that Allison announced adaptation of the fully automatic unit to lower-speed diesel engines.

Sales were made under the designation MT (Medium Truck). The early unit was the MT 25 for 250 hp—the division's start into commercial vehicle automatics—that was built, with improvements, until the early 1970s.

Allison's Chevrolet Series 5100 demonstrator tractor was among the earliest trucks fitted with the new CPT-4 Powermatic. The units blazed the trail for truck applications industry-wide and set Allison on the path towards its principal commercial markets.

Engineering manager Bob Schaefer (right) and sales manager J.A. Lane admired the chromed and enamelled cutaway of the January 1957 edition of Allison's new on-highway automatic. The unit employed a four-element torque converter, six forward speeds, one reverse.

Creating a Market

Creating the transmission was the easy part. Creating the market was another matter altogether.

For the military user, adoption of the crossdrive transmission was decided on the grounds of survivability and battlefield superiority, not cost comparisons or SFC data. For heavy-duty, off-highway machinery, the powershift's intrinsic and unique advantages over manual transmissions clearly offset its higher initial costs. Soon after introduction, the powershift was the standard. A big, off-highway truck was simply not sold without a powershift transmission, either Allison's or someone else's: the OEM energetically sold it to the customer.

But in the fiercely competitive and cost-conscious world of commercial on-highway transport, matters were not so simple. First, the new automatic transmissions typically cost from two-and-a-half to three-and-a-half times more than their manual counterparts. Second, to install the automatic unit, a truck builder might not only have to undertake costly modification of the powerplant installation, but supplant a profitable gearbox of his own manufacture. Third, for long-haul applications, the issue of fuel economy decisively favored manual gearboxes. Dealers energetically promoted vehicles, not transmissions, and price remained a crucial arbiter of sales.

The reality appeared quickly enough: of the 800 CPT-4s Chevrolet sold in 1956, they took back 600 from the dealers. By 1960, the Allison sales staff knew the job of work that lay ahead: they would have to convince the end user to demand Allison's automatic transmission from the vehicle makers. The product would have to be "pulled" through the sales cycle.

Nor was a persuasive promotion tactic far behind: the big, dramatic demonstration for the right kind of prospective user. An early target was trucks whose jobs are a mix of on- and off-road work—the transit concrete mixer, for example. By the early 1960s, Allison had won over some 30 percent of the transit mix business.

The Ultimate Vocation

"Then," says international sales director Al Schuette, "we found the empirical, all-time, ultimate automatic truck transmission application: the garbage truck. It's everything you need an automatic for: it's can-to-can, red light-to-red light, high speed to the landfill, where it becomes an off-road vehicle. Then in wintertime you put an A-frame on it and it's a snowplow. Plus, you've got drivers of every conceivable skill level."

The start was with city sanitation departments, recalls Schuette, where up-front costs were part of municipal budgets. "Initial cost was not so significant, but they hated the day-to-day headaches of manual transmissions—with axles, drivelines, clutches. Even a skilled driver tires after 2,000 to 3,000 shifts in an eight-hour day, and missed shifts are tough on a manual, straining everything from clutch to tires, adding maintenance costs and downtime."

As private refuse removal companies entered the market, the automatic's virtues became still clearer. A garbage truck may run 500 to 600 pickups each day, at $5 to $8 per stop. A lost day is expensive. Automatics are quicker, too, 20 percent or so more efficient than manual gearboxes.

User acceptance in other contexts was colored by emotional appeal. With the fire truck, notes Schuette, "you don't want to discover drivetrain difficulties when the alarm goes off." For the school bus, where the automatic's simplicity frees the driver to concentrate on control and safety, the question of cost gets rephrased at school

Perhaps the perfect illustration of end-user appeal for the automatic transmission is the school bus. In addition to its other generic advantages over manual transmissions, the automatic's easy driveability provides an indisputable margin of safety for drivers of every skill level.

Bottom: By 1977, when Superior Sanitation of Colorado Springs, Colorado, showed off one of its 26 Chevrolet C65 tandem-axle trash compactor trucks equipped with an MT 600 automatic, Allison was already on its way to a commanding lead in this specialized market.

Having worked as a truck salesman part time while at Michigan State in Lansing, ATD's director of international marketing and sales Albert R. Schuette joined Allison as a sales rep trainee in 1958. He has been a leader in shaping the division's on-highway marketing strategies, from the special demonstration to the international fleet caravan.

Named Allison general manager in February 1960 and a GM vice president the following March, Harold H. Dice came to Allison as assistant general manager in 1953 from the Electro-Motive Division. A graduate of the University of Illinois, Dice started with GM in 1929 at Delco-Remy in Muncie, Indiana.

board meetings: "What's the price of a child?"

Results tell the sales story: for school buses, Allison claims 70 percent of the market; city buses, 70 percent as well; garbage trucks, 60 percent; delivery trucks, 23 percent.

Some applications have remained resistant, notes Schuette. "We took the automatic out in the field 15 years ago to assess its suitability in the big semis. We didn't think we had easy entre. First, the drivers are good because that's where the pay is. Second, they're on the interstate in top gear 83.5 percent of the time. Third, the top quality manuals such as the Eaton Corporation's Fuller Division Roadrangers are tough competition.

"Still, there were values we wished to test. We put out 172 units in 28 fleets and measured them against manuals with all possible variables—altitude, engines, route stages, and the like. We did fine on many issues. But the bottom line was, for this vocation then, the automatic was simply too expensive."

The Low Man Syndrome Vanishes

During the maturation of the on-highway sales operation, there were some uneasy inhouse moments. Says Schuette, "Three times we felt like bottom dogs. The first came when we began: they hid us on the second floor at Plant 3, because the off-highway business was king. We didn't get invited to the Christmas party. The second time was when the corporation mixed the gas turbine sales group with ours: 'You guys are in garbage trucks, we're in airplanes.' The third time arrived with the merger with Detroit Diesel: 'You're in garbage, we're in semis.'"

By 1990, with 90 percent of the division's unit volume (not dollar volume, because military transmissions are so expensive), and future worldwide prospects generating great enthusiasm throughout the division, on-highway sales operations were genuinely integrated.

Allison automatics have been fitted to 17 percent of all applicable commercial vehicles in North America since inauguration of sales in 1956. In overseas markets, the corresponding figure is only 1.5 percent. But the offshore market is three times the size of North America's, and there lies one key to the division's future prospects. Allison has been systematically laying the groundwork of a transnational market strategy since 1987.

The First Decade

In 1956, the division began producing the XT-90 transmission and the CLBT-5640, a four-speed torque converter unit with retarder for locomotive switchers, and a forerunner of the 5000 series hauling transmissions that featured six speeds with torque converter, lockup drive, and input retarder. The CT-3340 and CLBT-4460 hauling transmissions and the HT-70 automatic went into

production. In 1960, came three new units: the CLBT-5940 Torqmatic, the CRT-3531 for front-end loaders, and the CRT-3321 for forklift trucks.

The Newill Era Ends

On February 25, 1960, division general manager Ed Newill retired. Harold Dice became general manager on February 26, and was elected a vice president of GM on March 7. Progress in both commercial and military transmission development continued at a steady pace.

The cycle of new, larger off-highway trucks required the ongoing upgrade of transmissions to match increasing engine horsepower for trucks whose payload rose from 40 to 65 tons. In February 1962 Allison introduced an upgraded CLBT-6060 transmission compatible with 600-hp engines to power these big trucks. Success of the CRT-3331 front end loader transmission in machines from 1 1/2 to 3 yards brought pressure from manufacturers to produce a lower capacity model for the 3/4 to 1 1/2 yard machines. With a new concept for the loader industry, production of the TT-2220 began in December 1962.

The 100,000th transmission came off the production line on October 15, 1959, at Plant 3. And, although production versions were several years off, by adding an automatic valve body to the CLBT-4460 transmisison, design-ers created the HT-70, an early entry into an important market niche—airport crash trucks, fire trucks, inter-city buses, and highway haulers.

As the 1,000th CD-850-5 retrofit transmission passed through Plant 7 in 1959, the division reviewed its sustained dominance of military vehicle installations. Among the decade's applications were the CD-500 from 1951 for the M41 Light Tank, the M42 Twin Anti-aircraft Gun, the M44

Having pioneered the application in 1953 at the request of Clark Equipment Co., Allison became a major supplier to builders of front-end loaders. In service with the Price Dredging Company in Miami, Florida, in 1955 was this Model HM Hough Payloader equipped with a CRT 3330 transmission.

and M52 Self-propelled Howitzers, the M8 Cargo Tractor, and the M75 Armored Infantry Vehicle. The CD-150-4 from 1957 had been fitted to the M56 Self-propelled 90mm Antitank Gun (Scorpion); the XT-1400 and the XT-1410 from 1954 to the M51 Heavy Recovery Vehicle (XT-1400-2A) and the M88 Medium Recovery Vehicle (XT-1410); the TX-300 of 1957 went to the eight-ton truck; and the XT-90 of 1956 to the M50 Multiple 106mm, Self-propelled Rifle (ONTOS).

In the early 1960s, component testing and fabrication of 12 pilots of the XTG-250 were initiated and the 25,000th CD-850 transmission was produced and presented to Army Ordnance. Development of the TX-100 continued; in May 1962 a $1.5-million contract was awarded for XTG-411 transmissions, followed in October by a $6.7-million contract for CD-850 transmission for the M60 tank.

Origins of the X-1100

Stimulated by West German developments in hydrostatic steering for the large battle tank in 1962, Bob Schaefer and Dale Hasler journeyed to

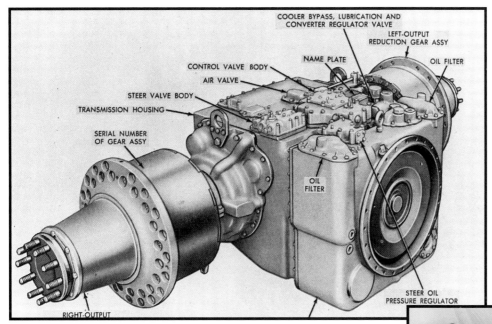

The XTG-411 transmission was part of the power train for a family of vehicles that included the M107 Self-Propelled Gun; the M108 105mm, M109 155mm, and M110 8-inch Howitzers; and the M578 Light Recovery Vehicle. Including units for repowered Israeli T54/T55 tanks in 1987, more than 16,000 XTG-411s were built between 1962 and 1987.

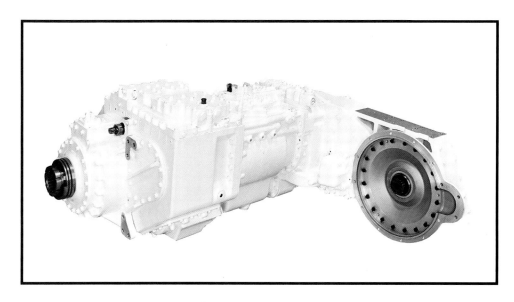

Complete with Hallmark card, this milestone CD-850 was ritually delivered to the Ordnance Corps on June 29, 1961. From left, are Ralph Forbes, Hugh Kirtland, John Storer, Herm Bowden, Roy Lynch, and Edgar G. Davis.

Detroit to present a proposal to Col. M.P. Wally, head of transmission activity at Army Ordnance. Wally endorsed the project, and after considerable development the X-700 program evolved into the X1100, Allison's "next generation" heavy tank transmission that would first see production for Chrysler's XM1 Main Battle Tank in 1979.

Hasler recalls some of the detours involved in the project: "Among our mistakes, we went to engine-driven steer, precisely what we'd learned with the CD-850 not to do. We didn't listen to Frank Blair. The Army thought it was great, that's what the Germans were doing. So we did it that way: with the X-700, X-300, and the X-500. It was all right, but we still had the problem that when you wanted to turn, you had to put your foot on the throttle. It was a little better with the torque converter: you could do it better but it still had that same characteristic. Finally, we took an X-700 and changed it on Blair's insistence: it was a job to change.

"Then we conducted a poll. We had people come to the Detroit Arsenal and drive pilots of each kind of steering mechanism. Everyone preferred the modified unit. Some of the merit of the X1100 is that it has the hydrostatic steering, whose capability and reliability go back to designer Howard Christenson."

A Bid on the MBT Program

In 1965 Allison undertook an Army contract for nearly $44 million for development work up to fabrication of pilot models in the

U.S./Federal Republic of Germany Main Battle Tank Program. Notes planning director Dallas Gritton, "That's the one that Chrysler won. In fact, the M1 is still in production today. GM could have had all of it, but we did not win that one. Of course the Allison X1100 transmission is part of that system, so we won a considerable chunk of it."

In July 1964 the Army accepted the prototype of Allison's newest powertrain, the XTG-250 and awarded the division a $2 million contract for production of XTG-411 transmissions. In September the gas turbine and transmission operations were consolidated for common use of

Among the shorter production runs was the XT-90 Series power train, of which only 221 were made in 1958-59, for this curious creation. Called the ONTOS, the M50 Multiple 106mm Self-propelled Rifle was designed for the U.S. Marine Corps to be used in support of assault operations.

While the Army's T10 twin-tractor, 84-foot-long transporter was used for other tasks as well, its most intriguing assignment was to haul the 85-ton, 280mm atomic cannon in the early 1950s. Powered by two 375-hp gasoline engines matched to Allison TX-500 transmissions, the vehicle could move at up to 35 mph. While visiting Aberdeen Proving Grounds, probably in summer 1954, Allison general manager Ed Newill (right) and soon-to-be GM president Harlow Curtice inspected a T10.

Another TX500 application was the T58 Truck (8x8) shown on the Durability Course at the GM Proving Ground one sunny afternoon early in the 1950s.

facilities. The transmission model shop at Plant 3 merged with the gas turbine aerospace model shop at Plant 8, and transmission drafting personnel were moved alongside of aerospace drafting there.

All transmission engineering areas, except the test department, were also set up at Plant 8. This consolidation continued for some nine years until transmission operations returned to Speedway. Transmission designers still lament the loss of their treasured model shop. Says one senior military engineer, "It's like working without your left arm after all these years."

CD-850 Retrofit Reactivated

Allison reactivated its retrofit line to modernize additional quantities of CD-850 cross-drive transmissions under a $7 million Army contract. Heading up the retrofit program was Paul D. Parke, assistant superintendent of production for ordnance transmissions. Covered under this second retrofit program were CD-850-4, -4A and -4B configurations which were updated to the -5 designation for gasoline engine-powered vehicles, and the -6A for diesel applications.

Also included was overhaul and retrofit work of other major CD-850 subassemblies. The last CD-850 retrofit program at Allison began in December 1958 and was completed in May 1962. During that period more than 2,000 850s were retrofitted under four separate contracts. The CD-850s for modernization came from several vehicles, including the M46, M47, and M48 Patton medium tanks.

Designed for 17-ton tracked vehicles, the XTG-250 power train featured a torque converter with automatic lockup clutch, four forward and two reverse speeds. Between 1966 and 1971, 2,610 XTG-250s were made, principally for the M551 General Sheridan Armored Reconnaissance/Airborne Assault Vehicle manufactured by Allison at the Cleveland Army Tank Plant.

Another Wartime Buildup

As the Vietnam conflict swelled to engulf more than 164,000 U.S. service personnel by the end of 1964, Allison's wartime capability was again tapped, this time to manufacture vehicles and ammunition at the Cleveland Army Tank Plant.

The operation was announced in May 1965:

"Allison, in a continuing program to widen its product diversification, begins operation of the Cleveland Army Tank

Automotive Plant. The new responsibility marks Allison's first effort in the design, development and production of complete military vehicles. The first of these tracklaying units scheduled for production starting in January 1966 are the XM551 Sheridan armored reconnaissance assault vehicle and the M109 self-propelled 155mm gun.

"Both vehicles will be equipped with Allison power trains, the Sheridan with the XTG-250 and the M109 with the XTG-411. Covering more than

Not usually parked on the front walkway, an M109 does extra-curricular patriotic duty in front of the Cleveland plant during Allison's management tenure there.

Before production began in 1966, prototype M109 (left), 105mm M108, and M114 command and reconnaissance vehicles (center) proved their durability and performance at the Cleveland Proving Grounds, near Hinckley, Ohio. The larger vehicles employed Allison's XTG-411 power train, the M114 incorporated the GS-100 hydraulic steering unit.

320 acres and with more than 2,600,000 square feet under roof—larger than Plant 5—the Cleveland plant was built during World War II by the U.S. Government for the Fisher Body Division.

"As a government facility, the plant was operated by Cadillac from 1950 to 1959, producing M41, M42 and M56 light tanks. In 1962 Cadillac resumed production activities, turning out M114, M108, and M109 vehicles. Allison . . . will assume jurisdiction of GM defense contract responsibilities now headquartered at the Cleveland Plant immediately."

From 1965 to 1970 Allison operated the plant, making not only the M551—the U.S. Army's principal vehicle in Vietnam—and the M109, but huge quantities of 81mm shells. From Cadillac's peacetime personnel roster of approximately 3,000 people, Allison's wartime staffing swelled to 15,000 at its peak.

Between 1965 and 1967 Jim Knott served as manager of Allison's Indianapolis plants. In 1967 Reuben Jensen was named division general manager, Bob Schaefer retired, and Robert Tuck was appointed transmission engineering manager as Schaefer's successor. Harold Dice continued as Allison Division general manager until his retirement in November 1967.

From a standing start in February 1945, the Allison transmission business had grown to some $115,000,000 per year for transmissions alone, of which approximately 65 percent was commercial, 35 percent military.

The Military Decade Reviewed

The decade's military transmission record was impressive, with two dozen active transmission applications. The TX-200 of 1960 was operational in the M113 armored personnel carrier, the M106 mortar

carrier, the M125 mortar carrier, the M132 flame thrower, the XM474E2 Pershing missile equipment carrier, Britain's FV432 personnel carrier, and the Federal Republic of Germany's HS30 personnel carrier.

The TX-100 of 1964 was installed in eight vehicle types; the GS Steer Unit of 1962 on three; the XTG-411-2A of 1962 on five types; and the XTG-250 of 1966 in the M551 armored reconnaissance/airborne assault vehicle.

Consolidating the AT-MT-HT Family

Certainly as vital to Allison's position in the transmission industry as any event to date was the division's sorting out of its penetration of the on-highway market.

The 1956 MT units for Chevrolet trucks had laid the groundwork, and the HT-70 of 1962 brought the Allison automatic to crash trucks, fire trucks, and vehicles of similar size. The third transmission type—the AT—would open the next arena of commercial applications.

Observed general sales manager John Hittle, "When we made the application for volume at that time, general manager Reuben Jensen said, 'You've got a 15-year-old product here (the MT). If you had a clean piece of paper what would you do?' Mark Fisher went with a cadre of draftsmen up to Hydramatic and they put together the design of what is the AT transmission today. It was known as the LT-240—Light Truck,

The M109 howitzer's gun turret rotated on a 103-inch-diameter, 250-lb ring, the largest such bearing then built anywhere in the U.S. Boring mill operator Roy Carr monitors the closely-programmed cutting operation at Cleveland early in 1966. The technology used in the big ring would be adapted by Allison engineers during the company's manufacture of rocket motor cases in Indianapolis.

Installation of its turret bearing ring completed, an M109 continues the assembly process, dwarfed by the huge interior of the Cleveland plant.

Reuben R. Jensen was named Allison general manager on September 15, 1967, following a two-year tour as general manager of the Hydramatic Division in Ypsilanti, Michigan. He joined GM in 1946 following engineering studies at the University of Nebraska, and remained at Allison until 1970, when he assumed a Detroit group vice presidency.

240-hp, four-speed transmission. They set a target price of $275 and tried to put together a project. There was inadequate volume to bring the price down so low. We decided then we would have an MT-340 (Medium Truck, 340 hp, four-speed transmission)."

"In 1966," adds Mark Fisher, "we came out with the new line of transmissions; the old MT-25 and MT-30 were in that 1966 introduction. Then, we'd always wanted a smaller transmission for some smaller vehicles. As that early transmission aged and we looked at new designs to get into the smaller transmissions, we had some help from Hydramatic. They actually made the first designs for the AT transmission (then called the LT). Based on the AT, we designed the MT, and in the 1970 model year came out with both of those units. And so we had the AT-MT-HT lines, all in part derived from the Hydramatic design of the AT."

Continues Hittle, "They added the MT and AT volume together and that was adequate justification for the project. At the time GM was involved with the GT404 gas turbine engine, and there was interest in a suitable automatic transmission for it. So we planned the HT 440—400 hp, four speeds. By combining these, three, we only had to sell 3,000 HTs a year in order to make the rest of the project a success. We are now selling 12,000 units a year."

The four-speed AT 540 was the first automatic ever developed specifically for vehicles in the weight class immediately above the size range of passenger car transmissions. Construction was completed early in 1970 on a 432,000-square foot addition to Plant 3 to provide adequate floor space for manufacture of the AT 540. From the time the first footing was laid to the first transmission off the line was 365 days.

What's in a Name?

The division's traditional transmission nomenclature was given a bit of corporate spin with the new on-highway family, recalls Hittle: "Reuben Jensen, who had preceded Jim Knott as division general manager in 1967, had spent considerable time with the Hydramatic Division. At that time Hydramatic was building their Turbo-Hydramatic 475.

"Jensen said: 'We have a bigger transmission, we need a bigger name,' and asked the staff to come up with a good one. The sales and engineering department couldn't decide. 'No recommendation?' Jensen asked. 'Then here's what we'll do. Add 300 to everything.' So the 200-hp unit (the 240, with the 2 for horsepower and the 4 for the number of gears) became the 540 because 540 was bigger than Hydramatic's 475. The 340 became 640; the 440 became the 740. We also got rid of LT (light truck) and went to AT (automatic transmission) because it suggested a broader range of applications."

At the Threshold

As Transmission operations approached what would be its most trying corporate challenges, its men and women looked back on their enterprise's first quarter century.

The achievements are a worthy roster of innovation and quality, including these benchmarks: first powershift marine gear, powershift for highway trucks, the crossdrive for tracked vehicles, hydraulic retarders incorporated into the transmission, fully automatic transmission for trucks, twin-turbine transmission for material handling equipment, variable input power torque converter for material handling equipment, and a durability test stand able to duplicate field operating conditions. Every tracklaying tactical vehicle built for the U.S. Army between 1946 and 1966 was equipped with Allison transmissions.

When Ken Harmon in the late 1960s compiled his list of the major innovations in the first 25 years of the heavy-duty automatic transmission business, he discovered that Allison had introduced 20 of the 21 inventions. The exception was Caterpillar's variable capacity converter, and that by scarcely a year ahead of the Indianapolis team.

The years just past were about to seem almost innocently carefree as Allison was swept into turbulent and troubling events. Some of the difficulties of the coming twenty years were born of seeds planted in the 1940s by Allison's own pioneer work. Others were imposed from the outside and would severely test Allison's mettle.

Among Allison's five highest-volume military programs, some 89,000 TX-100 transmissions were built between 1964 and 1987. The unit was adapted from a commercial design, primarily for the Army's M113 family of tracked vehicles powered by the GM6V-53 diesel engine. Light weight was a premium to enhance vehicle floatability, and the three-speed TX-100 was 150 lbs. lighter than its predecessor TX-200.

CHAPTER 9
Surviving

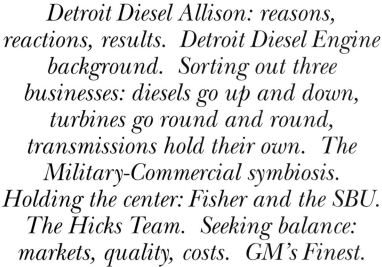

*Detroit Diesel Allison: reasons,
reactions, results. Detroit Diesel Engine
background. Sorting out three
businesses: diesels go up and down,
turbines go round and round,
transmissions hold their own. The
Military-Commercial symbiosis.
Holding the center: Fisher and the SBU.
The Hicks Team. Seeking balance:
markets, quality, costs. GM's Finest.*

The first Indianapolis-built Detroit Diesel Series 149 engine block was completed in August 1972. The 10,000th block left the line in January 1976, its serial number stamped into the metal by machine operator Donald Pierce (left) and acknowledged by foreman Daniel Duncan.

The September 1970 news release said: "GM chairman James M. Roche announced the consolidation of Detroit Diesel Engine Division with Allison. The new organization, Detroit Diesel Allison Division, is headquartered in Detroit. James E. Knott, GM vice president and former Allison general manager, has been named general manager of the new division. Knott said Detroit Diesel has an immediate and long-range need for additional diesel engine capacity that can be met with Allison floor space available at Plants 5 and 2 with more becoming available during the next few years. It should not be necessary to build any new floor space, while at the same time Plant 5 will manufacture diesel engine parts, he pointed out.

"The merger brings under one manager the diesel engines and transmissions which are extremely successful in industrial and off-the-road applications and are frequently installed as a package. Both product lines are profitable and the market is expanding. The merger will provide added sales volume and individual security that Allison needs, Mr. Knott said."

Originally built for the manufacture of aero engines, the 20 acres of floor space beneath the roof of Plant 2 influenced the corporation's planning for its 1970 merger of the Detroit Diesel Engine and Allison divisions. The Speedway factory became a major source of diesel engine components throughout the 1970s and 1980s.

The DDA Rationale

In 1969 senior corporation planners had assessed circumstances at GM's Detroit Diesel Engine Division and Allison Operations. A booming diesel engine market was straining Detroit Diesel's production capacity in Michigan; major engine customers were actually on quotas. Studies showed that new plant costs would make production unprofitable. The Detroit Diesel general manager was about to retire, and in Allison's Jim Knott GM saw a skilled and practical manager whose career had effectively combined engineering savvy, business sense, and success in meeting tough challenges.

In the context of GM's corporate history, the DDA merger possessed a curious inevitability. Robert M. (Bob) Clark, Allison Transmission Division general manager since 1987, explains: "Every corporation has its own neuroses. Within GM, one of ours revolves around floor space. We have a paranoia about creating more floor space and making use of every foot we own. At the time of the merger, in the corporate mentality it was a very good thing to put those two together and solve both problems."

The Detroit Diesel Pedigree

Motivated by Charles Kettering's interest in diesel technology for marine applications, General Motors began research into large diesel engine design in 1928. By 1934, the corporation's new lightweight diesel engine made history when the Burlington *Zephyr* streamliner opened Chicago's Century of Progress Exposition. In the spring of 1937, 75 acres of land were bought in Detroit and a 24,000-sq-ft plant was built with a separate test laboratory. The Detroit Diesel Engine Division was formed in 1938 to produce the Series 71 (the number denoting the cubic inch displacement of a single cylinder), a two-cycle, heavy-duty engine with innovative fuel injection.

During WWII diesel engines became indispensable for power generators, tanks, landing craft, and road building equipment. Production of the Series 71 swelled from 805 units in 1938 to 61,263 units in 1944. Increased power demands led to the "Twin," two engines geared to a single drive shaft, then the "Quad," four 71s similarly geared and used primarily on Landing Craft Infantry (LCI) vessels. The vast military exposure encouraged the product's acceptance in commercial applications, and a focused postwar effort established a distributor organization and retail sales coverage for marine and industrial units and replacement engines.

Allison and Detroit Diesel Meet

In 1946 Allison's sale of Roots-type blowers to Detroit Diesel became the first formal interaction between the divisions. Independently, both

Allison and Detroit Diesel stepped up product development. Oliver Kelley's transmission development work also provided liaison between Detroit Diesel and the emerging transmission group in Indianapolis.

Between 1948 and 1967 Allison's transmissions earned dominance in chosen markets. Detroit Diesel added engine lines so that it, too, came to lead its field: by 1967 its one-millionth engine was produced. Between 1960 and 1970, production tripled and the Detroit plant expanded to the Redford property boundaries.

An Uneasy Beginning

By January 1971 the Allison transmission staff had seen beyond the September merger rhetoric. Detroit Diesel quickly dominated Indianapolis operations with its large volume and expanding market. Allison veterans outspokenly characterize the period from 1971 to 1987 as problematic.

General sales manager John Hittle offers some context: "The best we'd ever been in our history was second cousins, and mostly we'd been third cousins. When we were with gas turbines we were a mundane, relatively small part. Our first million-dollar month didn't come until the early 1960s. There was nothing romantic about us, certainly not technologically, compared with turbines, and we were treated accordingly.

"After the wedding with Detroit Diesel, they were unquestionably the dominant part, gas turbine was the second, and, 'Oh yeah, down there are those folks who make electrical components for EMD.' These things, organizationally, had a tremendous impact on our people and created something of a 'martyr mentality.'"

James A. (Jim) Mitchner, director of customer satisfaction, felt that prior difficulties were emphasized by the merger: "One [problem] was compartmentalization—the tendency for authority to flow up and down between Indianapolis and Detroit within functions (finance, manufacturing, engineering). Cross-discipline exchange and teamwork were discouraged because of that vertical authority flow.

"Before 1970 Detroit did not exist: we were Allison in Indianapolis, gas turbines and transmission. We had the same thick walls then. After the merger, they were thicker, another layer added. The fact was, we were really three distinct businesses, and the third one was even more different than the other two. When the diesel operation got in deep trouble and required 95 percent of the effort from the top management of the combined division, that made it more difficult still."

Putting Things Right, Part One

In April 1982, came the announcement from GM that Allison's gas turbine business was to be sold to raise capital for use in GM's core automotive operations. That decision led to a massive reassessment of the division and a recommendation by prestigious consultants that if GM chose to stay in gas turbines, they ought to hire somebody who knew something about that business to run it.

In 1983 GM did just that. They split off the Allison Gas Turbine Division and hired one of that industry's proven leaders, Blake Wallace, to run the newly-independent division.

Along with its many profoundly positive benefits, separate division status for their gas turbine colleagues served to dramatize the disaffection rife within the transmission team. A senior transmission designer put it bluntly: "Then they merged us with Detroit Diesel. Gas turbines escaped and we were even worse off, an orphan of Detroit. As far as they were concerned, a transmission was something you bolt onto the back to help sell an engine. All the bosses were in Michigan: we were a headless outfit,

Facing page: The growing truck and bus markets for automatic transmissions drove major increases in Allison production from 1970 onward. Among the most familiar sights in Plant 3 were long rows of gleaming transmission cases. Jobsetter John Luper inspects valve body channels on AT cases in 1976. More than 385 machine operations prepared the cases before gears and other components were fitted.

with no management direction, and we really suffered from that."

Bob Clark agrees, in part: "I would submit that almost was the death knell for these businesses. Because gas turbines, transmissions, and diesel engines are three different distinct businesses, and we tried to treat them as one. When we did that, I don't think we did something good for any of them. Those of us in Indianapolis might have had the impression that the energies and resources were sapped off to the benefit of the diesel engine business, but I don't really believe that was true either. I think that we really mismanaged the lot of them to the extent that the diesel business got sold off."

The Light Before Dawn

But the situation was nowhere near so bleak as some believed, and genuine progress was underway that ensured the basic health and strength of the transmission operation.

Notes Jim Mitchner: "Because the management of the total division was in Detroit and spending a high percentage of energy on that end of the business, it permitted the organization in Indianapolis to come together as a team to do what it needed to do. There was a three-year period before we became a division, when we were operating as a strategic business unit (SBU). We worked as a team to run the business, and it worked. Almost by default we were forced to work in a mode of excellence."

That teamwork was spearheaded by Mark Fisher, who chaired the SBU from its beginning in 1983 until division status came in 1987. Fisher says: "We were far enough from Detroit that we were able to do some things just by working together. If we didn't work together, we were going to die. There were some very difficult times during that period. Then when there was an effort to sell Detroit Diesel—there were two tries, one with John Deere, then the later [and successful] one with Roger Penske—over two years' time, nobody paid a lot of attention to us [the transmission operation] and we had difficulties getting things approved."

Colleagues recall Fisher's work less modestly. Says one: "When Mark became director of engineering [in 1978], he remained a people person,

Mark Fisher earned his mechanical engineering degree from Purdue University in 1947 and came to work for Allison as a laboratory technician. He assumed engineering management positions of steadily increasing responsibility and retired in 1990 as ATD director of engineering.

a sharing individual from a communication standpoint. He had a willingness to work with all the organization and became an ideal director of engineering through the changes that we had to make to stay in business. He knew the business, knew the customers, knew the product, worked well with the customers. He was a very capable intermediary between all these elements, and was a dynamic chairman of the SBU."

Says another: "Fisher also led us to our biggest profit years. We turned in about 14 percent operating profit, some $100 million—nearly enough to offset the losses

that Detroit Diesel was accumulating. Under him the MQM (Materials, Quality, and Manufacturing) organization was restructured in 1983, a significant event in this business. We really anticipated by seven years everything GM is just now doing. But it was so radical that without Fisher, while it was well-intentioned, MQM would never have been."

Bob Clark credits the SBU operation as an important dynamic of management competence and independence: "The divisional resources were so focused on the diesel engine business and the possible deals to resolve it that Indianapolis was forgotten. And that was a mixed blessing, because people up there said, "Why don't you guys just go take care of that yourself?" That was when they tapped Mark Fisher to head the SBU.

"That SBU took decisions for this operation that were good. The area benefitted from some really first class leadership during that traumatic period. It was good local leadership, but all approval levels were still up there. The World Transmission, which had gotten to be a big part of our future, was put on hold. Nothing moved; we couldn't spend money because of the condition of divisional resources. It was a period of

While military crossdrives and off-highway powershift transmissions captured Allison's initial markets, the automatics swiftly penetrated new vocations to claim increasingly large portions of the company's unit sales. From 521 units in 1970 to 30,000 in 1978, the AT-MT-HT lines soon surpassed other product types to head the division's volume list. Assembler Francis Curry moves a completed AT 540 from assembly in the mid-1970s.

stagnation, but also a period in which the group here started to work together. And so it wasn't all good, wasn't all bad either."

A Detroit View of DDA

John Debbink, whose 36-year GM career included the power products group vice presidency, 25 years with the Chevrolet Division, and general managerships of the Delco Moraine and Inland divisions, watched the DDA episode closely and conversed regularly with key participants. He observes:

"There has been a maturing in the perspective from Detroit of what was going on in Indianapolis in the last five years, the comprehension that these people were in special businesses and should not be managed exactly like automotive businesses.

"They need to have the responsibility and authority of their own position to deal effectively with the competition in their market. They've been well supported, but should be able to play in their own ballpark. If the two divisions were not part of GM, they would stand out as stellar companies. Being a part of a giant, they don't get that recognition."

Not With A Bang

After separation of the Gas Turbine Division, four years remained of the DDA connection. Debbink describes that transition: "That left Allison Transmission and Detroit Diesel combined. It made some sense but it didn't work out well. There were already good arguments for separating them. It was increasingly apparent that there were separate interests and that the performance of the two divisions was quite different. We started losing heavily in the Detroit Diesel Engine part of it, while the transmission business was still making money. In fact, the transmissions carried the entire division."

Among the most successful Allison automatics is the smallest unit in the product line, the four-speed AT 545 introduced in 1980 for the medium-duty truck market and engines up to 235 hp. Assembler George Kemp prepares one of the first production units for post-assembly testing.

Meanwhile, Back on the Line

Defiant of the complex corporate
scenario unfolding in the front offices
from 1970 until 1987, the engineering,
manufacturing, service, and sales people
on the floor and in the field forged ahead
with the daily business of the world's
leading manufacturer of heavy-duty
automatic transmissions. They ran into a
serious thicket or two, but they scored
more than a few victories and laid crucial
groundwork for the division's vitality in
coming decades.

In the merger's first year, under Jim
Knott as division general manager, Don
Atwood as Speedway general manager, and Bob Tuck as transmission
engineering manager, the division's 500,000th transmission was built—a

John D. Debbink, who retired as power products group vice president in 1985, was among the senior GM executives in Detroit who strongly endorsed independent status for the Allison divisions in Indianapolis.

In May 1967 Robert M. Tuck succeeded retiring Bob Schaefer as transmission engineering manager. Among notable accomplishments during Tuck's tenure until 1978 was development of the X1100 power train for the M1 tank.

As off-highway operators sought efficiency through greater loads, truck and engine manufacturers responded. Trucks were exceeding 100-ton capacities and engine outputs soared, and Allison "grew" power trains to match. In 1971 Edward Brethman lowers a new TC 860 converter onto a DP 8961 transmission—a package able to handle 800-hp input.

DP 8961 for a 100-ton Euclid end-dump destined for a copper mine in Bougainville, Solomon Islands.

The new AT 540 production facility, a 432,000-sq-ft addition to Plant 3, including a fully-equipped 8,000 sq ft garage, was dedicated. Deliveries of the diesel version of the AT 540 began the following year.

Developing On-Highway Sales Strategies

Until the 1970s Allison's transmission progress had relied upon existing demand—the Army's tank needs, the off-highway truck and heavy equipment markets, for example. Says Al Schuette, "We designed, built, and applied well, but we didn't sell well, because of how our contracts developed—we met a demand. But where you had to create your own business, that was tough. Money was scarce, we didn't get the support."

Step Right Up, Folks!

As Allison sought to expand into the on-highway market, new approaches were clearly called for. Schuette recalls 1971 as the first year of the division's big demonstration fleet and national tour that

established a tradition and an effective sales tool—"the largest private fleet of demonstration trucks and buses of any manufacturer in the world."

The showy demonstration tactic proved especially effective with dealers, who welcomed opportunities to reach prospective new users. The sales staff imaginatively pursued effective display and "hands-on" events. In 1972 they staged the first "driveaway," with 38 Chevrolet trucks equipped with AT 540 transmissions touring the Indianapolis Motor Speedway. In 1974 the Power Parade Caravan Product and Country Music Show began a month-long 28-stop transcontinental tour, publicizing diesel engines and automatic transmissions.

The demonstration fleet would reach a dramatic zenith 18 years later with Caravan '89—a nine-nation tour that began near Madrid, Spain, in April and finished near Edinburgh, Scotland, in July. Led by a juggernaut Kenworth W900 line haul tractor that a Paris journalist dubbed "Colossus," the nine-vehicle caravan included typical vocation vehicles, from buses to refuse packers. At each of 16 enroute sites, regional Allison distributors arranged for additional local vehicles so there were ample opportunities for demonstration drives.

In February 1972 the HT 750 for diesels up to 400 hp and vehicles to 130,000 lbs was introduced, and production began in July on the HT 740, principally for buses and fire trucks. With introduction of four new HT

Inaugurating the 432,000-sq-ft Plant 12 with the first production unit of the newly introduced AT 540 transmission, assembler Jack Warner fits the bottom valve body element into place on July 8, 1970.

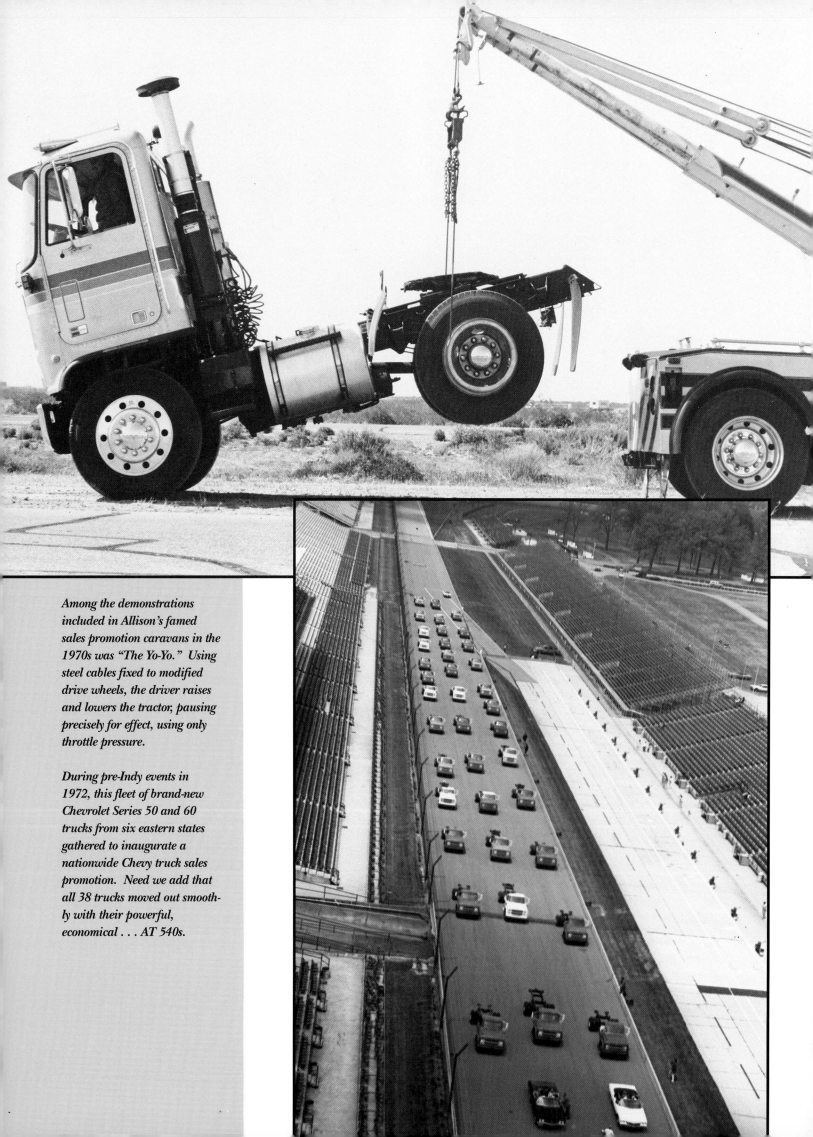

Among the demonstrations included in Allison's famed sales promotion caravans in the 1970s was "The Yo-Yo." Using steel cables fixed to modified drive wheels, the driver raises and lowers the tractor, pausing precisely for effect, using only throttle pressure.

During pre-Indy events in 1972, this fleet of brand-new Chevrolet Series 50 and 60 trucks from six eastern states gathered to inaugurate a nationwide Chevy truck sales promotion. Need we add that all 38 trucks moved out smoothly with their powerful, economical . . . AT 540s.

For a September 1971 meeting of the Indiana section of the Society of Automotive Engineers, Allison hosted a plant tour. SAE governing board member and Allison engineer Ken Harmon (left) reviewed the narration in advance at Plant 12 with Lloyd Runyon, superintendent of machining and assembly.

Not unlike Ringling Brothers' elephants before the Big Top, Allison's demonstration caravans featured a line-up of the vehicles (a dozen or so were routine) at each stop. This group assembled at GM's Mesa, Arizona, Proving Grounds, in the spring, c. 1975.

With the company's thrust into transnational marketing, Allison's Great Road Shows went overseas. The 1989 European Caravan was led by this Kenworth. European motorists unaccustomed to the proportions of American semi-trailer trucks agreed with the French newspaperman who named the rig, "Colossus."

In April 1974 the Indianapolis team built this 725-hp, 12-cylinder Series 149. Marking the occasion at Plant 5 were, in front, from left, foremen Ernie Vaughn and Jim Wood and production superintendent Howard Westbrook. From the left, behind, are Larry Ross, Mike Clayton, Bob Brown, Nick Rash, Larry Crews, and Bill Meadors.

and MT models, and the CLT 750, transmission sales in 1972 were the highest yet in division history, and in September the first Model 149 diesel engine was built at Indianapolis.

In December 1973 Don Atwood was named to head the new GM Transportation Systems Division, and was succeeded as Indianapolis operations manager by Edward Colby. A $7 million contract was signed in June for additional CD-850s, and in October, a contract for $6.4 million

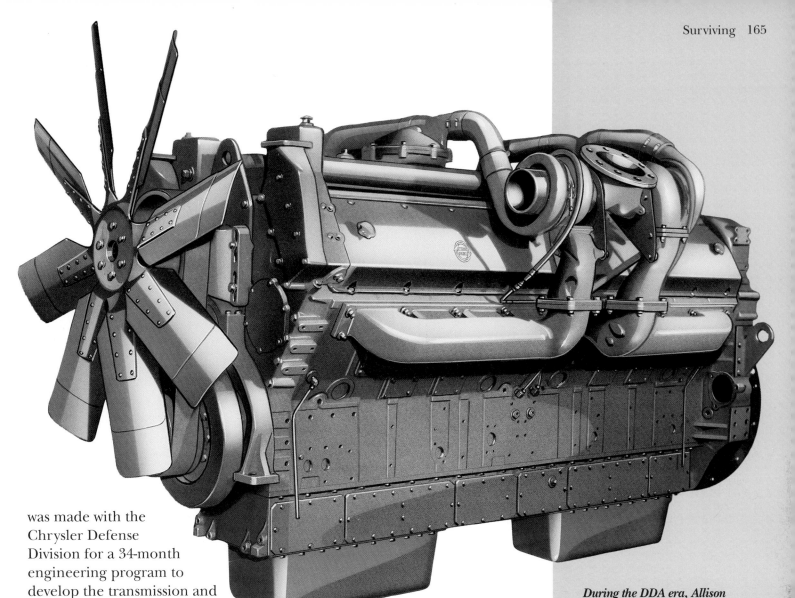

was made with the Chrysler Defense Division for a 34-month engineering program to develop the transmission and drive system for Army's new XM1 Tank.

Military and Commercial Symbiosis

Having achieved what the nuclear physicist knows as "critical mass," the transmission team grew increasingly adept at tapping their own resources.

"Very significantly," says Mark Fisher, "we've been helped in our technological development in the commercial market by our work with

During the DDA era, Allison employees soon accustomed themselves to the presence of imposing diesel engine elements on the line. Among DD's premier products was the Series 149 engine, like this two-cycle, 16-cylinder version that weighed 10,630 lbs and measured nine feet long.

In August 1974, Indiana Lieutenant Governor Robert Orr (left) joined with assembler George T. Kendrick (center) and operations manager Ed Colby to commemorate production of Allison's 750,000th transmission, an HT 750 for large line haul trucks.

the military. Tank transmissions are extremely complex—with their requirements for propulsion, brakes, and steer—and that technology has been most useful for the commercial side. Whether it's clutches or oil pumps, or whatever, it's basically transferable. So over the years the government has paid us for a great deal of development and [facilitated] our commercial work, reducing the R&D dollars we've had to spend for development."

Funding did not always come from the military, of course, and, consistent with trends at other defense firms, Allison in recent years has appreciated the need to expend its own resources on specific projects as well as critical research and development basics.

Commented military transmission engineering supervisor Ed Dewes: "When we built Plant 14, the Army put everything inside of it. They paid the whole engineering bill. That's not going to happen again. We have to start investing money in military transmissions. We never did before; all the money went into commercial transmissions. Bob Clark recognizes that and he has given us a lot of money. We're working today with GM money on two transmissions to replace the X1100. It's all GM money, and we're doing it ahead of time because we couldn't meet the schedule otherwise."

The exchange has been mutual. In one major crucial application, the basic Army truck fleets, a commercially-developed unit won the day. Dale Hasler begins the story:

Mark Fisher presents transmission engineering supervisor Ed Dewes with his 35-year service pin in July 1989. Dewes, who has specialized in design of military transmissions, was then directing the division's role in the Army's Heavy Forces Modernization (HFM) program.

"In 1958 the Army had tried several TX-200 automatics on the trucks. We came close to production then, but some fellow made a mistake in fuel consumption calculation. They had 20 vehicles made with automatics and manuals each way in 1958—M35-E7 and E8 trucks—at Fort Knox. When the fellows had to haul pianos, they took the stick shift. But when they went to haul the ammunition, they used the TX-200. We lost by eight percent on fuel consumption, but they admitted they didn't use the same routes.

"By 1973 we had been beating on [the Army] all this time, trying to get our transmissions into their trucks. So that year they ran another test on the 2 1/2 ton trucks, again by an independent contractor. They tested all the available automatics—Sunstrand, Clark, and our MT 640. It was a good test, with especially good work by Al Huevel, the engineer when we started the test, and Fred Vogelman, who wrote the report of March 1974.

"The results proved that our automatic performance was better than anybody else's; the stick shift didn't even come close; our fuel consumption was the same as the hydromechanical, depending on the

Among turning points in Allison's association with the U.S. Army was acceptance of the automatic transmission as the standard power train for trucks, as it had been for tracked vehicles since 1948. Playing a major role in the conclusively persuasive demo tests of 1973 was engineer Al Huevel.

Typical of the Army trucks in which Allison automatics dominate, particularly the MT 600 Series, is the M939 family, headed by the five-ton M939 cargo truck itself, built by BMY (formerly Bowen-McLaughlin-York) of York, Pennsylvania. The transmission is the MT 654.

Jim Knott (left), although his training was in aeronautical engineering and his Allison career had focused largely on aero engine issues, as DDA general manager from 1970 to 1978 earned high marks from his transmission colleagues for sound management over the division's wide range of challenges. At Knott's September 1, 1978, retirement ceremony, Mark Fisher presented a plaque with transmission images fashioned on bronze.

route. The others broke down several times, locked up on others. GE's transmission never showed up: it was so noisy they dropped out.

"Now the Army'd seen stone, and the word was: 'All trucks must have automatics.' Meanwhile, we already had a five-ton truck coming and an order for six MT 640 transmissions. Sunstrand had an order for six of their hydromechanicals. The general said, 'Cancel those and buy six more [Allisons].' That's the five-ton truck program. We had the increased capacity to meet the Army's requirements.

"GM sponsored the X-200 in 1968, the first time the corporation put out money for a military transmission. Everything else had been designed on government contract. Our memo said, 'We must do this if we're going to stay in the business.'"

More Plant Capacity

The outlook for automatic and powershift transmissions remained promising, so in 1974 construction was started on a 664,000-sq-ft addition—more than 15 acres—to the transmission production facilities, Plant 12. The largest single expansion in Indianapolis, the masonry and steel structure located directly across from Plant 3 represented a 50 percent increase in production capacity for heavy-duty automatic transmissions.

The V 730, the first new transit coach transmission in 25 years, was introduced in October 1975. During 1977 a record 77,279 commercial transmissions were shipped, a 17 percent increase over 1976, and the MT 643/653 DR (Deep Ratio) automatic transmissions were added to the line.

In 1978, with Jim Knott's retirement, Don Atwood returned to Indianapolis as division general manager, and Mark Fisher was named transmission engineering manager. Ed Colby remained general manager of Speedway operations until Bob Clark's arrival in 1979. Military contracts totaling $8.2 million covered the TX-100 for the M113, the XTG-411 for M109s, and the CD-850 for M60 tanks.

The 250,000th AT-MT-HT transmission was built in March, an HT 750 DR assembled at Plant 12, and the one millionth heavy-duty four-speed transmission, an AT 540, was delivered. Heavy-duty transmission shipments for 1978 exceeded 100,000 units, the largest number of automatic and powershift transmissions shipped in any single model year during 23 years of manufacturing transmissions.

Don Atwood, who would later leave GM to serve as Deputy Defense Secretary in the George Bush cabinet, was Detroit Diesel Allison's Indianapolis Operations manager from 1970 to 1973 (when he was named to head the new GM Transportation Systems Division), and the division general manager from 1978 to 1981.

DDA participated as one of several competing contractors in the development of the Army's M1 Main Battle Tank, whose design began "with a clean piece of paper" in 1972. While the vehicle production contract ultimately went to the Chrysler Corporation, Allison's won the transmission contract with its X1100 power train. In the fall of 1979, development team members visiting Fort Knox included, from left: Les Becker; Ed Colby, Mark Fisher, Don Guthrie, Ed Lundberg, Don Brindle, Lester Need, and Chrysler test engineer Bill Johns.

The first X1100 production unit was delivered in 1980, and by 1987 more than 5,000 were delivered, including this -3B unit. Designed for the M1A1 Abrams tank, the four-speed X1100 allows the 1,500-hp Avco-Lycoming turbine engine to accelerate the 65-ton tank from zero to 20 miles per hour in seven seconds. Transmission-integrated braking is equally efficient: from 40 mph in four seconds.

Military contracts continued satisfactorily in 1979: in May came agreements of more than $5.2 million for CD-850-6As for the M60-A1 tank and TX-100-1s for the M113. In June contracts totaling $24 million were added, covering CD-850-6As for the M60, XTG-411-2As for the M109, and spare components for XTG-1410-4s for the M88. At year's end, the initial production X1100-3B for the first production XM1 tank was shipped on schedule to Chrysler's Lima, Ohio, plant.

Beneath the impressive production figures, however, lurked the makings of a potentially lethal corporate problem, a problem that had

In Spring 1980 the first production X1100s were delivered to Chrysler's Lima (Ohio) Army Tank Plant. Accompanying the 4,300-lb transmissions to Lima for the presentation ceremony were DDA manufacturing manager Fred Best (left), and Ed Colby, Indianapolis Operations manager.

Among the M1 Abrams' design features is a suspension system that allows the hull to be raised for maximum ground clearance over rough terrain and lowered for minimum target presentation. The M1's main weapon is its 105mm cannon. While the manufacturing contract was won by Chrysler, the tank manufacturing operation was sold as the Land Systems Division to the General Dynamics Corporation in 1982.

been camouflaged by the divisional drama being played out in Detroit conference rooms.

The Iceberg Cometh

Director of planning and new business development Dallas Gritton describes the threat looming with the new decade: "In the early 1970s we had begun, without realizing it, to bury the on-highway automatics—the AT-MT-HT and V 730 transmissions. We had broadcast them to be at certain volumes and to cover a certain range of applications. By decade end that volume had not been realized; we were not making the money we had projected for the whole on-highway automatic family. To increase volume, we had begun to sell the product beyond the initial range of vocations that we had projected for.

"By 1980," continued Gritton, "the problem was undeniable. Most of the failures were not 'infant mortality,' which shows that it was not the plant that was out of control. The quality problem was durability. Transmissions would do 50 to 60 thousand miles of vocational usage and fail. There was a period of time where you could say with absolute assurance that every AT that left this plant for a garbage compactor would fail within warranty. We discovered that in our chase of volume to financially justify the project, we had put a whole lot of transmissions out there at risk in a much broader range of vocations than we ever anticipated.

"The good side was that we were incrementally building a volume base for our business, creating the very market demand that we're responding to today. And the world doesn't beat your door down demanding that you give them automatic transmissions. You have to go out and systematically find where these transmissions fit to advantage and value and then sell them to an end user as an overcost item.

Reassigned from his position as assistant chief engineer for quality assurance at Gas Turbine Operations to head up the Transmission Operations task force on quality in 1979, Bob Hicks supervised a comprehensive investigation and report called by some, "the turn-around for us in quality."

Fix or Flee

"The trade-offs in the equation were clear: having created the demand, were we going to fix the products and hold the market, or abandon the customer and walk away from the market? By the time the smoke had cleared in 1983, we had about $165 million in cumulative warranty problems— what we'd actually paid."

By 1979 customer complaints and warranty costs had escalated far beyond acceptable limits. Placed on special assignment from his position as assistant chief engineer at Gas Turbine Operations, Bob Hicks was named to head a multi-discipline blue ribbon panel to investigate and evaluate the transmission quality crisis.

After seven months of dedicated work, the Hicks Team reported to the divisional staff that about 50 percent of the failures originated with design and manufacturing problems within the factory. The remainder stemmed from poor application and installation and service problems. And the team offered strong preliminary recommendations on solutions.

Observes John Hittle, "The Hicks Study was really the turn-around for us in the quality program. Bob was a gentleman, and a fine mind. The total Allison operation began to make organizational changes, set up teams to work on problems, identify the root causes. As a result we've seen a 10-year period in which we were able to turn a very difficult corner, from really being in survival mode—although we didn't know it—to enjoying today the reputation with almost all our customers that our product meets their expectations. It took 10 years to do that."

The Path Not Taken

"Interestingly enough," observes Gritton, "in the same frame time Detroit Diesel was having the identical problem with their 92 series engine. And I believe the reason that we are still in business today and that they wound up as they did is fundamental: having recognized what our underlying problems were, we simply put our heads down, paid the price, and committed to fix the products with engineering changes. And we held that market, the base on which we run this business today.

"In contrast, Detroit Diesel said basically, 'It's either misuse of vocation or it's an OEM-related problem of not installing the product properly.' They had 50 reasons why it wasn't an engine-related problem. They dragged their feet, and didn't simply say, 'We'll eat it.'"

More Than Just a Fix

While the genuine commitment to deep and lasting institutional change would become the cornerstone of division policy, the first step was to begin to raise everyone's quality consciousness. That process was begun in 1980 by implementing a full staff-level quality assurance organization. Quality control had previously been a manufacturing responsibility, now quality was to permeate every aspect of the operation. Jim Mitchner was named the first director of reliability engineering.

Simultaneously, Mitchner and his colleagues inaugurated a radical new perspective on engineering and people-related issues at Allison. Says Mitchner: "We began to move into many different areas. For instance, we had been involved in a deterministic world of engineering until 1980. We would run one test and accept the results as proof of what successive repetitions would be. If we passed a 500-hour test successfully, then obviously we had a product.

"We moved from success testing to failure testing, because without the data point, you know nothing

Dallas Gritton, director of planning and new business development, joined Allison in 1954 while still a student at GMI (he graduated in 1959 and later earned his M.B.A. at MIT's Sloan School of Management). His varied Allison career has covered research, manufacturing, a tour in Warren, Michigan, as superintendent of vehicle fabrication while Allison worked on the M1 contract bid, transmission project management.

Jim Mitchner was named the Transmission Operation's first director of reliability engineering in 1980, and has led the division's commitment to a full staff-level quality assurance organization.

about the product; and with the data point you can use statistical analysis and other techniques. We changed to designing tests before we ran them and establishing from first principles what would constitute successful and unsuccessful results before the fact, not after the fact. That removes rationalization from the vocabulary of the engineer.

"Five years earlier I myself felt comfortable in explaining away the fact that one of our transmissions dropped out of a vehicle while we were running the test: 'Obviously, one of a kind.' With probabilistics you don't explain things away. You know that when something happens, something caused it, and you find the cause. You've got to deal with the data statistically; it's got to have statistic viability.

"You must understand what you need before you test. And then you test to determine if you meet your criteria. The results you get are just one set of data points. Then you manage these points statistically to see what the population probability is in terms of percent failure. All of that has happened at Allison since 1980.

"The revolution here in the last 10 years is enormous," concludes Mitchner, "and has had a lot more to do with where we are today than all that went before. The engineering community began the transformation. Young Bob Schaefer, then chief test engineer, and others implemented the concept. They organized reliability teams and reliability managers for the products. They established a statistical training section in engineering. Phil Ross became the first person that began to train all our engineering people in statistical method."

In one sense, the transmission group had little choice. Says John Hittle: "When we got to the early 1980s with nothing forthcoming, we finally were able to get the organization to acknowledge the indebtedness to the engineering department. At the same time, with no new product, we recognized that there was a technological gulf in our future. We had to bridge that until something new came along—the World Transmission. That was the generator of our quality effort."

The SCAAN Project and Applications

Accompanying philosophical change came concrete advances with immediate utility. One such advance was under development when the Hicks Team returned its findings, and it could not have been more cogent. Mark Fisher described it:

"Part of our earlier problem lay in the fact that we'd gone for a broader market but didn't have a good system for following what we were doing. Generally, ours is not the base transmission. But we needed to control the installation so it would be correct. Over the years our decision-making about particular installations has evolved into a reasonably user-friendly computer system—SCAAN (System for Computerized Applications Analysis)—with some 150 units worldwide.

"It's a wonderful sales tool; we make thousands of these SCAANs each year, right from the dealer's terminal. And now the installation checkout is being computerized as well. We can make application decisions in a week instead of several. If a proposed installation is within SCAAN limits, that's sufficient, but if not, the project comes in here so that the supervisor of applications makes the decision. An overly complex decision process would limit us too much. SCAAN was developed in house, beginning in the late 1970s, and we're still improving it."

Coping for Survival

The next step was tougher yet—true organizational change to fit the division for the enormous tasks it faced as a leader defending its turf but

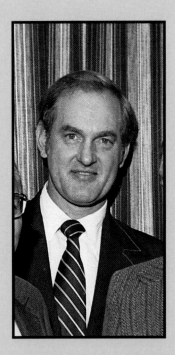

Sometimes called "Young Bob," to distinguish him from an illustrious Allison engineering predecessor of the same name, as chief test engineer Bob Schaefer earned particular distinction for his work in reliability and statistical training for the engineering staff.

Developed to refine and expedite the process of matching transmissions and applications, Allison's System for Computerized Applications Analysis—SCAAN—links ATD headquarters with distributors and original equipment manufacturers (OEM) worldwide. In addition to its obvious advantages for problem prevention and swift communication, SCAAN has proven a persuasive sales tool much praised by dealers and distributors. Al Albin puts the program through its paces.

needing to conquer new ground to survive in the coming century.

Facing several fundamental crises simultaneously, transmission operation leaders rose to the challenges directly.

Says Bob Clark: "From the time that I got here [in 1979] and began to understand what was happening, I went on a campaign to split the three businesses [diesels, turbines, transmission] up and let them run independently, both in how we organized internally and in campaigning the corporation to get the gas turbine people spun off so they could do their own thing. Ultimately we succeeded. I think that was a keen piece of business. Essentially they have been doing better ever since."

John Debbink concurs: "We recognized then that the transmission operation should be separate. We proceeded to separate the transmission business at the same time we did the current venture with Roger Penske for the Detroit Diesel engine business. That left the transmission people free to do their own engineering, to be totally responsible for their business, concentrate on their markets. It was absolutely the right thing to do. The transmission people were doing a remarkably good job from the engineering standpoint to get their act totally in focus."

The Baldridge Award Competition

The transmission group's work on quality culminated in the corporation selecting them as GM's representative for the 1988 Baldridge Award competition. Among 60 or so competitors representing America's leading manufacturing and service companies, the Allison Transmission Division placed among the final contenders.

Named in honor of the late U.S. Secretary of Commerce Malcolm Baldridge and established under the National Quality Improvement Act of 1987, the annual Baldridge Award is administered through the National Institute of Standards and Technology to recognize quality achievements of U.S. companies and publicize quality strategies. Following nomination, candidate companies undergo a rigorous self-examination and assessment by a distinguished Board of Examiners, including site visits and detailed audits.

Says Debbink, "There were people in the corporation who had never heard of Allison. Some of the car people kind of blinked their eyes, 'Who are these people?' Then on a very careful evaluation, they were judged as the best in the corporation to represent us in the Baldridge competition.

"The [heavy-duty transmission] business depends on having not just good technology, but having the best. [For example], ultimately the military has to have the best. It doesn't do you any good to have the second best engineering company. In the car business, you can be second best and still sell a lot of cars. In automatic transmissions, unless you're first best for most of your customers, you don't sell anything. Particularly under Mark Fisher they've done a superb job of engineering over the years. With the tremendous effort and improvement they've made on quality, they really have done an excellent job."

Approaching Independence

The three Allison enterprises in Indianapolis wrestled with their unique and complex difficulties. They were not alone in the turbulence affecting much of the General Motors organization. America's largest industrial enterprise itself struggled to adapt to swiftly-changing global economics. Personnel and organizational changes in Detroit exhibited uncertainty, even agitation, and the effect radiated to Indianapolis.

Ludvik Koci served as DDA division general manager during 1982 and 1983. Named DDA director of diesel engine and transmission engineering in July 1979, Koci was previously assistant chief engineer of development at EMD, where he had begun his GM career in 1960 following graduation from GMI in 1959 and the earning of his M.S. from Michigan State.

In January 1981 Don Atwood was named group executive of GM's Electrical Components Group, and was succeeded as DDA general manager by Harold L. "Pete" Smith, as the Allison's division-wide quality and pride program got underway. In July Bob Clark moved up to general manufacturing manager from the Indianapolis operations manager position as Ed Colby assumed the task of planning overseas marketing.

In September John Hittle became the manager of quality assurance for Speedway; Jim Mitchner took on the new post of reliability and quality engineer; Robert Boehmer was named plant manager for Speedway; and Joseph D. Hester became plant manager in Maywood.

In corporate restructuring in April 1982, Don Atwood was named head of the newly-realigned Worldwide Truck & Bus Group. DDA was added to the group that included the GM Assembly Division, Chevrolet, and GMC Truck & Coach. In September DDA assumed responsibility for operation of the diesel engine manufacturing plant in Moraine, Ohio, with some 900 employees.

In October 1982 Ludvik F. Koci was appointed DDA general manager to succeed Pete Smith, who retired in November. In May 1983 GM set up a new operating group, Power Products and Defense Operations, formed and headed by David S. Potter, and to which the DDA Gas Turbine Operation was briefly attached. The following November, DDA Transmission Operations earned the Ford Motor Company "Q1 Preferred Quality Award" for exemplary quality performance.

Whatever the tumult among their colleagues and the corporation, Allison's transmission team was undaunted. They were readying themselves to take on the world.

Continuing a happy relationship begun in 1955 when Henry Ford II first asked GM to provide automatics for his company's trucks, executive vice president Harold Poling (holding plaque) of Ford's North American Automotive Operations in 1983 presented Allison with Ford's Q1 Preferred Quality Award. Representing Allison at the Dearborn, Michigan, presentation were, from left, quality assurance manager John Hittle, plant manager Howard Chambers, and national account manager Roger Day.

CHAPTER 10
Challenging

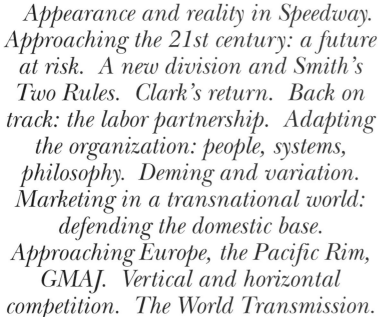

Appearance and reality in Speedway. Approaching the 21st century: a future at risk. A new division and Smith's Two Rules. Clark's return. Back on track: the labor partnership. Adapting the organization: people, systems, philosophy. Deming and variation. Marketing in a transnational world: defending the domestic base. Approaching Europe, the Pacific Rim, GMAJ. Vertical and horizontal competition. The World Transmission.

In this series of cutaway renderings of ATD's on-highway product line in 1987, differences in torque converters, gearboxes, and valve bodies are clearly visible. Converters are at the left side of each rendering, gear trains to the right, valve bodies below. With maximum engine input limits and typical applications are: [A] the AT 545, to 235 hp, pickup and delivery, bus, one-way rental, fire, and utility trucks; [B] the MT 643, to 250 hp, P & D, beverage delivery, dump, fire, short haul tractor; [C] the HT 740, with retarder, to 445 hp, fire, line haul, intercity bus, liquid bulk hauler; [D] the HT 754, with hydraulic controls, to 445 hp, linehaul, liquid bulk hauler, refuse, transit mixer, oil field truck; [E] the HT 755 ATEC with electronic controls, to 445 hp, logging, dump, refuse, transit mixer, oil field trucks.

For much of the decade that began in 1980, Allison's Transmission Operations led a dynamic and sometimes precarious double life. To the outside world of customers, suppliers, subcontractors, and others, the company appeared to be going about its business in the customary manner. The anticipated flow of quality products remained high, customer service needs were met promptly and fairly, and evidence of able marketing and product development was ample.

A Lurking Crisis

The appearances of 1983 were deceptively conventional. Lud Koci was in his second year as division general manager, Ron Dostal served as manager of Speedway operations, and Mark Fisher was in his fifth year as transmission engineering manager.

In July Plant 12 turned out the 75,000th HT transmission, an HT 740 for an Army M977 series truck. The first fully automatic transmission for on/off-highway hauling vehicles, the CLBT 750, was radically improved and redesignated the CLBT 754. In December the CLT 9880 transmission was introduced for oil and natural gas production in the People's Republic of China.

In Indianapolis some 7,000 Allison men and women were contributing to the manufacture of five general classes of heavy-duty transmissions (including marine gears), Electro-Motive Division locomotive parts, Detroit Diesel Series 149 engines, and replacement parts for Allison Transmission and Detroit Diesel Engine product lines.

Active production covered a wide spectrum. Off-highway hauling transmissions included the CLT 3461, CLBT 754, CLBT 5000/6000 Series, DP 8000 Series, and the CLBT 9000 Series. Cycling transmissions included the Series TT/TRT 2000/3000/4000 and the Series CRT 5000. The automatic transmission line comprised the Series AT 500, MT 600, HT 700, and V 700. Five military transmissions were active: the TX-100, XTG-411, CD-850, XT-1410, and the X-1100. The reverse and reduction marine gears were offered as standard equipment on all Detroit Diesel marine engines.

Six plants in the Speedway area were in operation. Plants 1 and 4

A

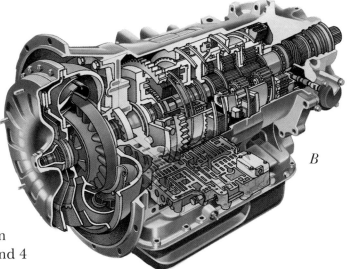

B

housed the World Training Center; Plant 2 manufactured assembly line and service parts and was the worldwide packaging and shipping center. Plant 3 was both the Transmission Operations administrative headquarters and principal transmission manufacturing facility, supplemented by Plant 12. Plant 14 was devoted to the X1100 transmission for the Army's M1 Tank. The Allison Gas Turbine Division's nearby Maywood Plant 5 continued to provide most gears used in Allison transmissions.

Beneath these disarmingly conventional appearances churned powerful forces of change, forces that would galvanize the company's leaders to carry their enterprise into a new era of challenges greater than Allison had yet faced.

While they were interacting dynamically for the entire period, the company's responses to those forces came together most dramatically in the achievement of independent division status in December 1987. The light of that event illuminates much that preceded and follows for the enterprise known now as the Allison Transmission Division of General Motors.

Division Status

Following his first Allison tour at Allison in 1980-83 as manager of Indianapolis Operations and general manufacturing manager, Bob Clark had maintained contact with a network of colleagues there. Late in 1987 the corporate decision was made to implement an Allison Transmission Division (ATD) and candidates were advanced for the position of general manager.

Smith's Two Rules

When the issue came before GM board chairman Roger Smith, participants recalled, he asked two questions. Has the fellow that's going down there had any transmission experience? No, came the answer. "Well, whoever goes down there is going to have transmission experience." The backup candidate was named. Then came the second question. Has the man ever been a general manager? No, came the answer. Smith is reported to have replied: "I'm giving you guys two rules: whoever goes down there has to have transmission experience and he must be a current general manager. We're not going to start a new division with a new manager."

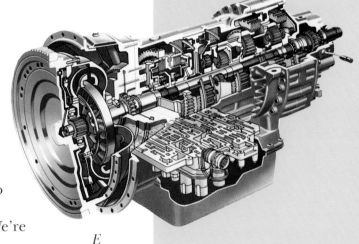

E

C

D

From January 1981 until retirement in August 1990, Roger B. Smith was GM board chairman. Smith policies included investment in state-of-the-art manufacturing technology, improving quality, and lowering costs—all consistent with his ultimate endorsement of such major Allison programs as the World Transmission. On his last Allison visit before retirement, on July 20, 1990, Smith toured ATD plants.

Reminiscent of their crucial first meeting after Clark's appointment as ATD general manager in December 1987, UAW Local 933 chairman Bob Boone and Bob Clark met again often in Clark's now-properly-refurbished Plant 3 office throughout 1988.

"Well," recalls Bob Clark, "there was only one person in the corporation who fit that specification, and that was me. It was an untimely move personally, I thought. I'd only been at Rochester Products for a short time, but the next thing I knew, I was on my way to Indianapolis."

On the first of December 1987 ATD became a GM division. As soon as Clark arrived, he and his staff set about creating all the functions required to run a proper division. They began by consolidating the financial staff previously shared between Detroit and Indianapolis.

Remembers Clark, "Dallas Gritton said when I arrived that it didn't matter who came. If he were on site here in Indianapolis and empowered to make decisions, a well-trained orangutan could have a success here. We went to work then, and we tried to determine what did we want to do with the business, where did we want to go."

Restoring the Labor Partnership

An early priority was to rationalize relationships between the local union and management. Because the issue's resolution characterized much that was to come in the months ahead, Bob Clark's account of the issue is helpful:

"We had an adversarial relationship of long standing, an historic, legitimate confrontation. We didn't have a contract, although the national contract had been signed six weeks earlier. Most UAW locals had settled, but ours wasn't even meeting. I talked with Ron Dostal and asked if I could meet with Bob Boone, the local UAW chairman, in the morning. Yes, he'd meet with me. So we came into this room [Clark's office]. There was no furniture, no pictures on the wall. The door was charred, because we'd had a fire here and they hadn't fixed it yet.

"Boone and I brought two chairs in and we talked. I told Bob that I had been in Dayton, Ohio, working at Inland Division when I watched us burn Frigidaire right to the ground because management knew they could never get together. I believed that we had the capability between us to burn *this* place right to the ground. This business could be gone in five years.

"There was no question that we could absolutely kill it and we'd all walk away. In fact, that was the direction we were headed. We were going to wipe this business out. Because World Transmission, the day I came here, was intended [by the corporation] to be installed at Moraine, Ohio, in the old Frigidaire plant. Those people would do anything to get a job.

"Or, I believe that we have a business here with the potential to be the jewel in the GM crown. We could grow rapidly and we could be an absolutely booming business. And I believe that all the people that are going to make that decision are in this room. I'd like to hear what you're going to do.

"There wasn't a word in here. We just looked at one another, for a long time. Then he talked for about 30 minutes and everything he said made sense. And I told him so. After leaving this office, Bob Boone called the negotiating group together—they hadn't even been meeting—and they went 30 straight hours and we had a contract. It was ratified right after the first of the year."

One outcome of that first year of union-management dialogue (and long contemplation by union officials who were initially skeptical about management's ability to fulfill the true spirit of the document) is a "statement of commitment" on how both groups thought they should act, how they should treat each other, how they should treat people, customers, suppliers.

Statement of Commitment for the Allison Transmission Division

Mission: The people of Allison Transmission Division are dedicated to: the creation of and aggressive leadership in worldwide markets for heavy-duty automatic commercial and military transmissions, systems, and related products; excellence in design, manufacturing, marketing and service for the mutual benefit of our customers, employees, business partners, share-holders, and community.

Beliefs: We believe this mission requires us to fulfill customer expectations with quality goods and services of superior value; to work together in an environment of mutual respect and trust that demonstrates integrity, to result in continuous improvement in all that we do.

Strategies: This mission will be achieved by being responsive to market needs; listening to the internal and external customer; teamwork; technology innovation and engineering excellence; improved participation of our people through the development, enhancement, and utilization of their skills, thereby providing value that exceeds customer expectations.

Symbolic of the accord that allowed the new division to optimistically forge future programs was the first union and management joint leadership conference in February 1988. One outcome of that meeting was the execution of a statement of beliefs relating to the all-important World Transmission project. From left, UAW World Transmission coordinator Tony Cooper, UAW Local 933 chairman Bob Boone, ATD general manager Bob Clark, and ATD WT director Don Brindle.

With division status came Bob Clark's strong emphasis on communication, including frequent opportunity for informal interchange. Typical was a spring 1990 retreat for senior staff at Indianapolis' Eagle's Crest. Seated are director of operations Wally Renn, left, and general manager Bob Clark. Standing, from left, are Art Tregenza, director of personnel and public relations; Jim Mitchner, director of customer satisfaction; Ron Dostal, director of materials management; Skeets James, divisional comptroller; Dallas Gritton, director of planning and new business development; Don Brindle, World Transmission program manager; John Hittle, general sales manager; John Buttermore, director of engineering; and Neal Mansfield, Electronic Data Services account manager.

It took us days of hammering at each other over in a conference room in Plant 1. The credo was first shared with everyone in the division in a joint ATD-UAW holiday greeting for 1988.

Changing a Culture

Part of the fresh approach emphasized by Clark and his management team was the acknowledgement of prior management failures to recognize the core role of *people* in any corporate undertaking. Reflects Clark, "We chased direct labor: we focused on reducing the direct labor content of the product, and it just led us down all the wrong paths. One day, we woke up and realized that what we'd been doing all those years was wrong, just wrong, and that we have to undo all the things that organizations have learned and to learn something brand new if we're going to compete in the world.

"That's the big thing we're about right now. We have tons of work to do. It will take us three to five years to get totally productive."

As part of the division program to enhance productivity through communication, seminars and conferences encourage the interchange of ideas. A 1988 leadership conference brought together leaders from management and the union in a two and one-half day working conference, called by Clark, "Maybe the best conference of that nature I've ever attended. Everyone participated. In teams at small tables, we developed and shared findings, helping to break down the departmental barriers and learning to work legitimately across functions—a major cultural change in this organization."

Bob Clark and his senior managers are convinced that any plans for the division's success depend completely on Allison's *people* and their effectiveness as an organization with purpose and values. They have devoted significant energy and time to developing a suitable environment for people and ideas. A major factor in creating that environment has been a charismatic teacher with a puckish smile and lots of common sense.

The Deming Phenomenon

Born in 1900, thinker and teacher W. Edwards Deming has been widely praised in corporate circles for his effective counsel on contemporary business values and operation. Invited by Gen. Douglas MacArthur to Japan during the post-WWII reconstruction movement, Deming is credited with introducing many of the ideas there that have made Japanese business so successful in recent years. In 1981 he was "reintroduced" by a White Paper aired on NBC Television, "Japan Can, Why Can't We?"

In the 1986 edition of his book, *Out of the Crisis,* Deming says: "Long-term commitment to new learning and new philosophy is required of any management that seeks transformation. Management will in time be judged not by the quarterly dividend, but by the plans and innovation with the aim to stay in business, to protect investment, to ensure future dividends, and to provide jobs and more jobs through improvement of the product and service for the future.

"One requirement for innovation is faith that there will be a future. Innovation, the foundation for the future, can not thrive unless the top management has declared unshakeable commitment to quality and productivity."

Such thinking seems powerfully relevant to Bob Clark. "I started working with Deming six years ago at Buick-Oldsmobile-Cadillac, when Bob Stempel [then GM president, named chairman effective August 1990] asked me to meet with Deming and see if we could use him in the powertrain organization there. It was an unforgettable experience." Clark hadn't been back at Allison three months before the division had its first four-day Deming Seminar.

"Deming teaches the philosophy of management, simple and straightforward, common sense stuff," says Clark, "but it's a very good package. The main thing Deming does is, he is an enabler. By buying into the Deming philosophy a person can, with honor and dignity, go talk with a colleague to do the things that are right for the business. The process doesn't have to be a personal risk. It legitimates work in teams, to find sound ways, to eliminate ineffective ways. And it confers the right to voice your opinions about what's wrong without personally putting yourself at risk."

Deming seminars include teams to work on local issues with a diverse group that represents different disciplines and the process creates a huge start for that group of people when they get back to work. Again, Bob Clark: "We took a critical mass, over 3,000 of our people, through the seminar in a year and a half. Deming has been key, and continues to be key."

One immediate result of Deming's counsel has been a basic change in Allison's personnel evaluation system. Jim Mitchner explains: "He says you must understand the differences between people. If you have an average—half the people above, half below—that's normal variation and doesn't make the people below the average second-grade citizens.

"An appraisal system that grades people and puts them in boxes is wrong, destroys people. We changed ours last year. We realized that we were tampering with these people's lives by trying to evaluate a person's performance on the basis of the output of the total system, when in fact that person's performance had five percent of the output and the rest of the system had 95 percent."

Admired by academics and businessmen alike as one of contemporary America's most astute thinkers and teachers, W. Edwards Deming at age 90 continued to forcefully advocate his view that management must nurture people and "declare unshakeable commitment to quality and productivity."

At the January 1990 Detroit Charles F. Kettering Award banquet, James Polak was honored for his work in designing the World Transmission, whose gear arrangement permits six speeds in the space previously needed for only four. Jim Polak, here joined by Mrs. Polak and GM chairman Roger Smith for a celebratory portrait, retired in 1985 after 37 years of service with Allison.

Division Status Indeed

Their new-found division status and Detroit's revised perspective on Allison especially delighted transmission veterans. Their long campaign to obtain corporation support for the World Transmission project illustrated the phenomenon.

From the kernel of award-winning transmission designer Jim Polak's sophisticated six-speed automatic bloomed the idea for Allison's third-generation product line, the World Transmission, planned for phased introduction beginning in February 1991. With such a sweeping program came the need to solicit suitable policy and financial support from the corporation.

Recalling seemingly endless charts, slides, memos, and trips to Michigan, Jim Mitchner wryly summarizes a process: "We have been at the WT transmission program since 1984, and in the process of this little division getting approval to spend $250 million for the project, we ended up making something

Manufacturing development engineer Richard A. Ordo was the first Allison recipient of GM's "Boss Kettering Award," in 1986. Ordo, a 1974 GMI graduate and 20-year Allison veteran, specializes in materials handling systems. His award-winning invention facilitated robot processing of World Transmission components.

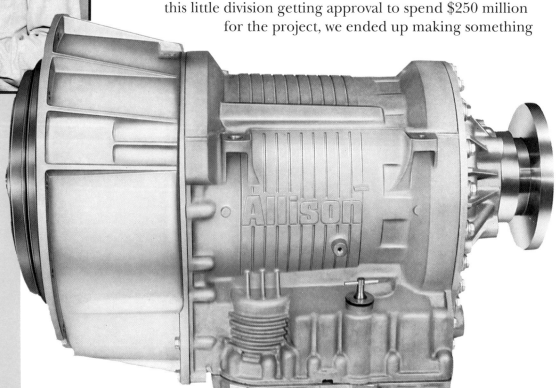

The first career engineer to be named GM board chairman, 56-year-old Robert Stempel succeeded retiring chairman Roger Smith in August 1990. Stempel, widely respected throughout the auto industry for his decisiveness and innovation, had been president since 1987 and has been a strong supporter of both ATD and Allison's Gas Turbine Division. Guided by Don Brindle (left), Stempel inspected a WT exhibit during a 1989 visit to Indianapolis.

General sales manager John Hittle graduated from GMI in 1959 in mechanical engineering, studied at Xavier University and Marion College, and tried his hand at teaching before joining Allison in 1966 as a project engineer. Hittle became manager of export sales in 1975, on-highway sales manager in 1976, and manager of quality assurance in 1980.

like 75 different presentations to various elements of the corporation. Sometimes we repeated presentations to the newly-appointed corporate executives who had just replaced the earlier ones we spoke to. That's got to change. Nobody can afford that. And I think the corporation knows that. To our credit, in all those 75 presentations, we got the same response: 'That's a good project, you ought to go do it.'"

The trips to Detroit changed remarkably when Bob Clark arrived. Says John Hittle: "It was awesome when we went to appeal for additional money to [then-GM president] Bob Stempel on the WT. Clark talks to the secretary and the staff like old friends, helps himself in the kitchen, and says, 'please bring us some coffee.' We've never had contacts like that before.

"There was no question that the president of General Motors knows this guy and has complete faith in his position. We never had that before. First of all, we didn't know we needed it because we were always sheltered from the bigger picture."

Other operational advantages to division status quickly became evident. Al Schuette notes: "Two things happened when Detroit Diesel was removed: first, they eliminated a group vice presidency (John Debbink's); and second, Allison's potential [was seen] to coincide with policy

Facing page, bottom: After its phased introduction in 1991, the World Transmission is expected to offer ATD a strongly competitive product line not only for established markets, but for Europe, the Asia Pacific Rim, and Latin America, where performance will determine Allison's future. The prototype boasts an uncluttered, futuristic look.

directions that genuinely interest GM, particularly Allison's international prospects

"At GM, the financial department is supreme: we may not have understood that, but in Detroit, no one ever doubted it. The New York treasurer's office is the center. In order to do what we want to do internationally, with outfits that have been transnational companies a long time—like Daimler-Benz, Volvo, Iveco—we needed different banking terms, positions of legal entitlement, and the like. Now, we get the help we need."

Parallel Advantages

In some instances, division status merely affirmed or accelerated policy decisions begun during the time of the SBU.

Notes Mark Fisher: "In late 1970s, we couldn't put anything into production because it was too long, too much money, or something, always a problem. The process was that we'd hand over the drawings for a new product to manufacturing engineering and in six months the costing would be done: and the costs would be too high, the tooling would be too high, or whatever. And the process was pretty much mutual. We began to realize that without a new product, we weren't going to be in business very long.

"In the early 1980s, after this had happened several times, we were planning to bring out the X-200 military transmission. The costs were projected to be $105-110 million, some $75,000 per transmission. This was a commercial venture: we were going to put our own money into this thing as a replacement for the transmission we'd been making for years (some 90,000 units) for the M113 personnel carriers.

"The government was unwilling to fund the program. So we assembled an engineering group—process, product, and reliability people—to work on the project. In about five months, they came back with a $17-million bill and $50,000 piece cost. That was pretty reasonable and happened pretty quickly.

Reshaping Communications

"This change didn't happen swiftly, not until we actually started working together. We decided to combine product design and production engineering by making the respective engineers all product engineers, all to be located in the factory. There wasn't enough room on the floor, so we got some trailers and put the service, reliability, product, and production engineers all right outside the door to the area where the process engineers worked. After a few months, it got to working pretty well. Everybody began to work together, get things done, to be more responsive. By 1984 we were on the way.

"We put all the AT-HT-MT folks together, all the off-highway people, pretty much the whole system. Then, we did much the same thing with the WT (before we had the formal WT team). More recently still, we've begun the Deming people-process, a philosophy that's starting to take hold. There are other things besides Deming at work here, of course, but we've had lots of successes that show hourly and salaried people working together can really make a job work, really make a difference."

One of the managerial problems was that the Detroit Diesel Allison staff had been organized functionally. All the engineers reported to a chief engineer in Detroit; the manufacturing people reported to a manufacturing director in Detroit, and the same with finance, so that the full operation became functionally oriented.

The Allison divisions are among the State of Indiana's most important institutions. The active part played by both the company and its individual employees in community affairs have linked it closely to Indianapolis and other cities around the state. Plant visits by mayors, state and national legislators, and governors are not uncommon. But they still provide pleasant opportunities for ceremony, like this 1987 tour by Indiana Governor Robert D. Orr (left), hosted by Ron Dostal and Mark Fisher (right).

"We are still trying to repair those scars today," believes Fisher, "because that made us less than an effective team locally. You couldn't do the things across organizations that an organization should do in terms of people development, and all kinds of activities that are better done as a team were difficult to accomplish because everything had to go up there for approval, then come back down.

"As an independent division, we can accomplish things now in an hour that used to take us two months. Our responsiveness was very poor; our customers would agree. We just couldn't get things done. That's one of the reasons people here now feel much better about themselves. They're empowered and can get things done, can work as a team."

Allison's military program managers concur. Says Ed Dewes: "Even though we still have a lot of things to get, the fact that we are now a separate division and we have a manager here in Indianapolis who sees things on a day-to-day basis is a real plus. I really see the change in our attitude to military business. In the past, it was presumed that 'the Army will pay for it,' no matter what it was, but that's no longer true. And the X-200 was a good example. We put it into production smoothly without the Army paying for it up front."

The Growth Goal

"We decided early on," observes Bob Clark, "that one of the principal things to do is to grow our business. We started to look at our niches. We are a niche marketer, not 'all things to all people.' We try to sell our product where it provides value to the customer. Most of the people who buy our product use it to make money. We can demonstrate to most users that they make money by using our products. In the niches that we have been working in the U.S., we predominate.

"If you want to grow your business, unless the businesses you serve are growing, you'll stay flat. In fact, you have a chance to lose because you attract competitors. So we began to analyze the markets of the world. We're pretty good in transit buses, city buses. But Europe makes an enormous number of buses compared with the U.S.; it's a big market over there. So we want to maintain our domestic market and grow as that market grows. One of our first priorities is to defend our home markets, because they are certain to be invaded from Japan and from Europe.

"And so we have our transmissions in vehicles that are coming in here to compete with our domestic vehicles. We're defending our market by putting our transmissions into the Mitsubishis, the Hinos, the Ivecos, and others. We make a major effort at that which protects the domestic market."

That policy provides the base for Allison to grow in the niches in Japan, the Far East, and Europe that they've grown in the U.S. "And," continues Clark, "we believe that we can use the same techniques in those markets that we've used here—which is to sell the end user, because he's the guy who makes money."

In 1987 the team set to work strongly to do the necessary things to start growing the overseas market. The division took a majority position in General Motors Allison Japan (GMAJ), started a joint venture in Brazil, and launched a major effort into Europe.

To launch a Brazilian joint venture to manufacture Allison transmissions in Sao Paulo— TransAllison, S.A.—in December 1988, ATD general manager Bob Clark, accompanied by John Hittle, toured the Brazilian facilities and met the operation's key people. TransAllison was organized to meet a growing demand for automatics in Brazil, particularly for buses.

Tending to the Day-to-Day

While the future was in the making, Allison's steady accomplishment was uninterrupted.

In March 1986 the 1,500,000th Allison commercial transmission, an MT 653 automatic, was delivered to Navistar International Corporation for installation in a dump truck for the State of Indiana's highway department fleet. In May the 100,000th 700 series transmission was shipped to DDA's distributor, D.G.S. in Mainz, Germany. This CLBT 754 transmission was installed in a Liebherr autocrane. By September a record 63,184 AT and MT series transmissions for Model Year 1986 were shipped. The previous high was 1979's 62,363 units.

Heading for the second million, the 1986 celebrants in Plant 3 seem to have plenty of energy. Gathered cheerfully around the chosen MT 653 housing are, from left, Mark Fisher, Ted Worrell, Dick Burley, Chuck Eyster, Steve Mitchell, Ron Dostal, Pat Amor, and Richard Fox.

Marketing Comes of Age

As global operations continue to grow in importance, Allison's engineering culture has expanded its vision as well.

Ken Harmon observes: "Our business began as engineering dominated. We still have technical leadership, but more and more our success is a matter of marketing. In fact, in 1989 for the first time ever, our product plan was set by marketing, not engineering. One index is the fact that we tried for 20 years to crack the rental truck market: last year we did it."

Pacific Rim Markets

Occasionally marketing zest may run afoul of international politics. The 1989 government crackdown on the New Democracy movement in Beijing illustrates the risk, says Al Schuette: "Allison has secured the best presence of any GM entity in China; an office in Beijing, a full-time employe, a technical center with 12 employes, and we're working on licenses to build products there. Of course we don't want to do business with bad people who abuse people, but there are a lot of good people there too. The system's at fault, but the people are nice people. If Tiananmen Square hadn't happened, the following week we'd have had the first automatic transmission bus on the streets of Beijing.

"And elsewhere in the Pacific, our U.S. domestic experience has served us well. We don't have to learn all over. In Japan, the truck market is expanding. In the Philippines and in India, we're testing. Maybe five years, ten years, but we want to be there. With the Japanese government encouraging development in these regions, who'll get the business? Certainly the Japanese. And the trucks will have Allison transmissions. Today, by quantity or price of product, Allison is the only horizontal company to do business with all the four Japanese majors in our industry: Hino (Toyota); Nissan Diesel; Fuso (Mitsubishi); and Isuzu. All build trucks and buses, all make their own engines, frames, axles, cabs. The one horizontal exception is Allison's automatic transmission.

Preparing for the October 1989 Tokyo Motor Show, Al Schuette, who alleges that during 1989 he spent more time in 747s than anywhere else, checks over the Allison display on opening day. He may also have been pondering the catchy slogan, "Safe, Simple, Sperior."

Japanese OEMS & Allison

Says Al Schuette, "Allison's strategy—whether trucks come from Nissan in Tokyo or from International Harvester in Louisville—is that as long as they have an Allison transmission, it shouldn't make any difference. The North American truck producers say, 'If they come, we'll just nameplate them and sell them.' So we don't see tremendous amounts of competitive response coming from North American producers against competitive imports from Japan. I think that in the next five years we are going to see similar inroads in trucks that we've seen in cars in the last 10 years. That's why we're working as hard as we are

A highly visible symbol of Allison's continuing progress in the vital Japanese Home Market is the Tokyo Fire Department's growing fleet of fire trucks. This smartly turned out Isuzu, like all the department's new trucks, includes an AT 740.

in Japan to make very sure that the Allison transmission is released on Japanese OEM-produced trucks."

Adds Dallas Gritton, "We see tremendous gains beginning there to sell to the Japanese domestic market, as well. Every new fire truck acquired by the Tokyo Fire Department, for example, now carries our HT 740 transmission."

International Military Markets

Fresh approaches to old markets continue to yield prospective long-term business. As planners pursue the Army System Modernization (ASM) program—including the replacement for the X1100—it is becoming clear that there may be international market opportunities for military transmissions not previously identified. In the next ten years one goal is to broaden Allison's market base for military products.

At the same time, defending markets already won remains urgent. Notes one engineer-manager: "Only so many X1100 military transmissions come down the road in a given ten-year period of time: you're either in or you're out. The military product is roughly one-third of the Allison business base and certainly important. We intend to be *the* North American presence for large track-laying military transmissions."

Price Competition

Several venerable Allison transmissions have uncertain futures, heightening the urgency to develop productive new markets. "Even though such products have served the company well, they're old," says Dallas Gritton.

"The outlook is not obvious. We don't see any significant shifting going on within the markets. We're down to operating maybe 15 to 20 percent of the volume we were operating on seven to eight years ago. Obviously, our capacity is under-utilized, which limits our ability to control cost.

"[Simultaneously] our customer base is under serious competitive pressure from people like Komatsu and Caterpillar. And, as best we can, we've been working with our customers. For example, three years ago Komatsu offered two of our best accounts an immediate 25 percent price reduction to accept their products. Our customers came to us and we matched that, and within 30 days were offering another 10 percent. In that six-to-eight year period of time, we went through a 35 percent price reduction on a commitment basis on some products. We don't make much money, in fact, we don't make any money in that arithmetic. But we did hold on to market position in the customer group that we were with.

"How long can you do that? We must decide on new product entry—it's more modern technology, looking into a continuously depressed market condition, a tough decision."

The Need for Profitability

A special problem is also described by Dallas Gritton—the emergence of serious competition where Allison had not been challenged before. "Since there's no natural market for the on-highway automatic transmission, and very little competition on the military side, this business tended to grow over the years without the benefit of competitive impetus.

"Reversing the original situation, in recent times we've tended more to create the market than fulfill demand we created. Our piece of the action today in heavy-duty on- and off-highway transmissions and military transmissions approaches $1 billion a year. The segment that we compete in would be somewhere between $1 billion to $1.5 billion a year and we turn out to be the dominant supplier worldwide. We maybe have 80 percent of the available market for the types of applications for our products.

"Now, we envision much more serious and extensive competition than we were forced to recognize in the last 30 years. We really should have

Allison's leadership in off-highway power transmission has been sustained for more than four decades by application in new vocations and constant improvement in existing products. Introduced in 1963, the CT 6061 installed in this oil field drilling rig is representative of the vocations in which the division is the acknowledged leader.

made a great deal more money than we have in the last four years. If you're going to have a monopoly, at least at the end of the day you should be able to bail the money. We've always been chasing the buck."

The Long Term

Allison planners, however, are anticipating the long haul. Continues Gritton, "This is a long-term business. I could see this business in 10 years, with the international opportunity, increase its size two to three times. Our

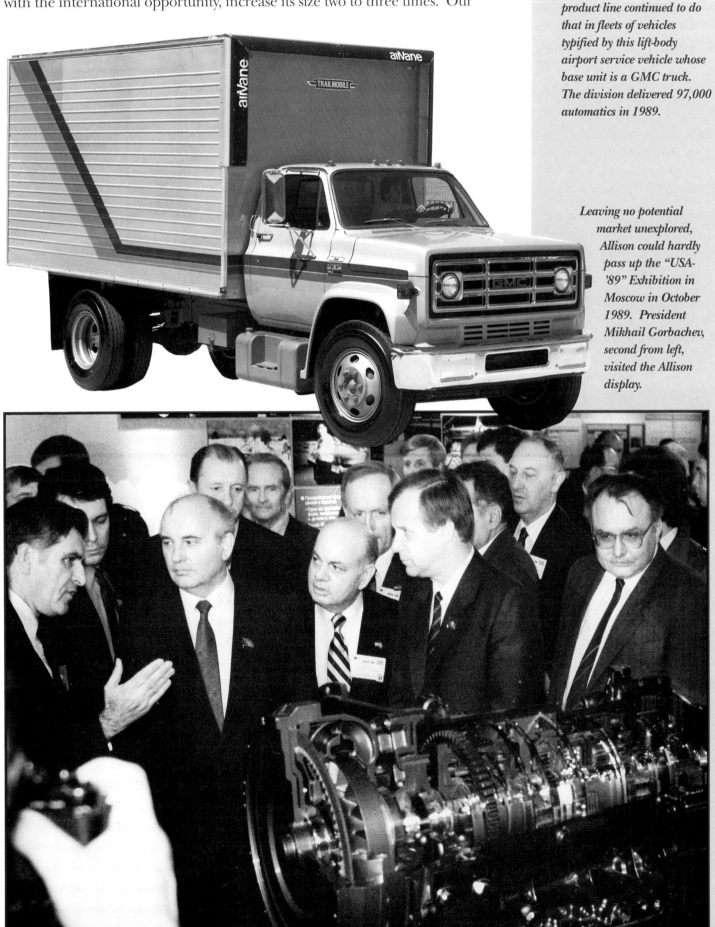

Left: Even while confronting the global challenge of multi-national marketing in the fast-developing European and Asia Pacific arenas, Allison must maintain and expand the domestic market share it has achieved. The AT-MT-HT product line continued to do that in fleets of vehicles typified by this lift-body airport service vehicle whose base unit is a GMC truck. The division delivered 97,000 automatics in 1989.

Leaving no potential market unexplored, Allison could hardly pass up the "USA-'89" Exhibition in Moscow in October 1989. President Mikhail Gorbachev, second from left, visited the Allison display.

goal is to make that happen. The automatic is the growth opportunity. There's no reason why we shouldn't be able to do the same thing in Europe that we've done in North America."

Penetrating Europe

Among the great challenges, not only to Allison but to businesses worldwide, are the monumental changes underway in all of Europe. Huge new markets with new and different rules present themselves. And those companies who do not effectively plan to compete may simply be shut out altogether.

"We need to look at selective partnerships," believes Gritton. "Europe 1992, for example, is a challenge. All our manufacturing facilities are here in North America and yet we see a significant growing market in Europe. Do you pick a partner and co-join a manufacturing base between the North America and Europe? Or joint venture, perhaps even some non-contract type? This is a major issue for every significant manufacturer in the world."

In 1974 Allison created a European Office and now sells almost 15 percent of its product overseas, through five regions—Europe, Japan, Brazil, Southeast Asia, and Latin America outside Brazil. Concludes Gritton, "Our focus on strategic planning has to do with the whole European market and Asia's Pacific Rim."

Their shoes aren't dusty, so they probably didn't break up all that concrete themselves. Nonetheless, the milestone ground-breaking entitled the WT Team to a moment in the limelight. From left, Moses Gray, Bob Clark, John White, Ron Garrett, Don Brindle, Dan Ellabarger, Tony Cooper, and Ken Sutton.

Tomorrow, the World

The Allison Transmission Division approaches the 21st century with an array of assets and capabilities unmatched in the world. A team of more than 5,500 uniquely talented, trained, experienced, and committed engineers, managers, design, manufacturing, service, and support personnel. Five modern headquarters buildings covering 3.8 million square feet and housing its industry's most advanced design, test, and manufacturing facilities. A global network of 20 regional and area offices and 2,100 dealers and distributors. Partnership in the nation's largest industrial enterprise, the General Motors Corporation. A track record since 1946 of manufacturing more than two million commercial and military transmissions.

Planned for phased introduction alongside the current product line beginning in 1991, is the World Transmission. The WT series, a comprehensive line of sophisticated, electronically-controlled, precise-shifting transmissions offers greater flexibility, operating economy, and lower installed cost in more applications than anything on the market.

Illuminating these formidable resources is the bright heritage inaugurated by Jim Allison and so honorably burnished through 75 years of innovation, imagination, and integrity—the power of excellence.

Headquarters for Allison's International Sales/ Service Region I (Europe/Middle East/ South Africa) is located in the elegant General Motors Building in Sliedrecht, The Netherlands. As the division refines its strategy for participation in the European Community from 1992 onwards, the Region I office will acquire expanding significance. Courtesy, Flying Camera, Eindhoven Airport

Allison Transmission

Domestic

Central Region

Regional Office - Location 1 § Indianapolis, Indiana

Location 2 § Naperville, Illinois

Location 3 § Danville, Indiana

Location 4 § Plano, Texas

Locaiton 5 § Lewisville, Texas

Location 6 § Edmond, Oklahoma

Eastern Region

Regional Office - Location 1 § Marlton, New Jersey

Location 2 § Marietta, Georgia

Location 3 § Morris Plains, New Jersey

Location 4 § Glen Allen, Virginia

Location 5 § Melbourne, Florida

Location 6 § Indianapolis, Indiania

Location 7 § Clementon, New Jersey

Location 8 § Brewerton, New York

Location 9 § Duluth, Georgia

Western Region

Regional Office - Location 1 § Fremont, California

Location 2 § Westlake Village, California

Location 3 § Aurora, Colorado

Location 4 § San Bernardino, California

Locaiton 5 § Laguna Niguel, California

Location 6 § Scottsdale, Arizona

Canada

Allison Transmission
General Motors of Canada Limited,
London, Ontario, Canada

International

International Operations (Home Office)

Allison Transmission Division
General Motors Division
Indianapolis, Indiana

Region I

Europe/Middle East/South Africa

Albania, Bulgaria, Czechoslovakia, Hungary, Italy, Malta, Romania, Yugoslavia

Regional Office
Allison Transmission Division
General Motors Nederland B.V.
Sliedrecht, The Netherlands

Northampton Office
Iceland, Republic of Ireland, United Kingdom
Allison Transmission Division
GMOD Administrative Services Corp.
Northamptonshire, England

Paris Office
Algeria, Benin, France, Gambia, Guinea, Ivory Coast, Mali, Mauretania, Morocco, Niger, Portugal, Senegal, Spain, Togo, Tunisia, Burkina Faso
Allison Transmission Division
General Motors France Automobiles S.A.
Argenteuil Cedex, France

Russelsheim Office
Austria, Federal Republic of Germany, Poland, Soviet Union, Switzerland
Allison Transmission Division
GM Service Gmbh
Russelsheim, Federal Republic of Germany

Sales and Service

Antwerp Office
Belgium, Luxembourg
Allison Transmission Division
Division of GM Continental, N.V.
Antwerp, Belgium

Finland Office
Suomen General Motors OY
Espoo, Finland

Sweden Office
Sweden, Norway, Greenland, Denmark
GM Nordiska, A.B.
Haninge, Sweden

Athens Office
Allison Transmission Division
Athens, Greece

Johannesburg Office
Allison Transmission Division - Southern Africa
Johannesburg, South Africa

Region II

Japan

Allison Transmission Division - Japan
General Motors Allison Japan, GMAJ
Tokyo, Japan

Region III

Brazil

Allison Transmission Division
GM do Brazil LTDA
Sao Paulo, S.P. Brazil

TransAllison S/A
Joint Venture GM Brasil X Moto Peca
Transmissoes S/A
Office: Sao Paulo, SP, Brazil
Factory: Sorocaba, SP, Brazil

Region IV

Asia/Pacific Region

Singapore
Allison Transmission Division
Jurong Town, Singapore

Australia
Detroit Engine and Turbine Company, O.E.M.
Division
Tottenham, Victoria, Australia

Peoples Republic of China
Allison Transmission Division
General Motors Overseas Corporation
Beijing, Peoples Republic of China

Region V

Latin America

Allison Transmission Division
Coral Gables, Florida

Argentina
Allison Transmission Division
Buenos Aires, Argentina

Mexico
Allison Transmission Division
Department of GM Mexico S.A. de V.C.
Mexico, D.F.

Allison Transmission Division

North American Distributors

Central Region

Central Detroit Diesel-Allison, Inc.
Liberty, Missouri

Clarke Detroit Diesel-Allison, Inc.
Cincinnati, Ohio

Delta Detroit Diesel-Allison, Inc.
Memphis, Tennessee

Inland Diesel, Inc.
Butler, Wisconsin

Interstate Detroit Diesel, Inc.
Minneapolis, Minnesota

Peninsular Detroit Diesel
Dearborn, Michigan

Stewart & Stevenson Services, Inc.
Houston, Texas

United Engines, Inc.
Oklahoma City, Oklahoma

Western Detroit Diesel-Allison
Addison, Illinois

Eastern Region

Atlantic Detroit Diesel Allison, Inc.
Lodi, New Jersey

Coastal Detroit Diesel/Allison, Inc.
Jacksonville, Florida

Connecticut Detroit Diesel-Allison, Inc.
Middletown, Connecticut

Covington Detroit Diesel-Allison, Inc.
Greensboro, North Carolina

Florida Detroit Diesel-Allison, Inc.
Miami, Florida

Johnson & Towers Baltimore, Inc.
Baltimore, Maryland

Johnson & Towers, Inc.
Mt. Laurel, New Jersey

Keystone Detroit Diesel-Allison, Inc.
Wexford, Pennsylvania

Massaro Detroit Diesel-Allison, Inc.
Tonawanda, New York

Penn Detroit Diesel-Allison, Inc.
Philadelphia, Pennsylvania

Power Products, Inc.
Wakefield, Massachusetts

Western Branch Diesel, Inc.
Portsmouth, Virginia

Williams Detroit Diesel-Allison
Midwest, Inc.
Brunswick, Ohio

Williams Detroit Diesel-Allison
Southeast, Inc.
Atlanta, Georgia

Western Region

Alaska Detroit Diesel-Allison, Inc.
Anchorage, Alaska

Pacific Detroit Diesel-Allison, Inc.
Portland, Oregon

Sierra Detroit Diesel-Allison, Inc.
Berkeley, California

Smith Detroit Diesel/Allison, Inc.
Salt Lake City, Utah

Spokane Diesel, Inc.
Spokane, Washington

Stewart & Stevenson Power, Inc.
Commerce City, Colorado

Valley Detroit Diesel-Allison, Inc.
City of Industry, California

Williams Detroit Diesel-Allison
Southwest, Inc.
Phoenix, Arizona

Canadian Region

Cullen Detroit Diesel Allison, Ltd.
Surrey, British Columbia

Harper Detroit Diesel, Ltd.
Toronto, Ontario

Marlin Detroit Diesel, Inc.
Ste. Foy, Quebec

Midwest Detroit Diesel, Ltd.
Winnipeg, Manitoba

Waterous GM Diesel, Ltd.
Edmonton, Alberta

Waterous Power Products
Calgary, Alberta

European Region - Region I

Afrima Division Verswijver Energie
Antwerp, Belgium

Agricel - Division of Tractores
Lisbon, Portugal

Allied Diesel
Damascus,
Syrian Arab Republic

Baan Hoffman Diesels B.V.
Gorinchem, The Netherlands

Berner & Larsen A/S
Oslo, Norway

BTR Power Products (Pty.) Ltd.
Kempton Park,
Republic of South Africa

Carlin Middle East
Cairo, Egypt

Consolidated Equipment Company
(Pvt.), Ltd
Karachi, Pakistan

Diesel Engineering, Ltd.
Tel Aviv, Israel

Diesel Und Getriebe Service GmbH
Mainz-Hechtsheim,
Federal Republic of Germany

Etn. C. Verswijver NV
Antwerp, Belgium

Farradj & Company
Amman, Jordan

Gatewood Engineers, Ltd.
Newport Pagnell,
Buckinghamshire, England

General Navigation & Commerce
Dubai, United Arab Emirates

Hellenic General Motive Corp.
Athens, Greece

Hema Anadolu Traktor Ve Satis A.S.
Istanbul, Turkey

Industrimotor AB
Stockholm, Sweden

Inglomark Markowitsch & Co
Vienna, Austria

Distributor Network

International Distributors

Kesko Oy Machinery Division
Helsinki, Finland

Mitchell Diesel Limited
Nottingham, England

Munradtech, Ltd.
Slough, Berkshire, England

Penven, S.A.
Beauchamp, France

Power Diesel Products, Ltd.
Kalkara, Malta

Saudi Diesel Marketing
Dhahran Airport, Saudi Arabia

Sterki AG
Wolfhausen, Switzerland

SWE Diesel Services (Pty.) Ltd.
Windhoek (Southwest Africa),
Namibia

Taha El Sayed El Roubi & Co.
Khartoum, Sudan

Talbot Diesels Ltd.
Iver, Buckshire, England

Thomas Schmidt A/S
Bagsvaerd, Denmark

Transdiesel, Division of Casli, S.A.
Madrid, Spain

Turner Diesel Ltd.
Glasgow, Scotland

Velar H/F
Reykjavik, Iceland

Yusuf Ahmed Alghanim and Sons
Kuwait, Arabian Gulf

Japan - Region II

Summit Engineering Co., Ltd.
Seoul, Korea

Summit Engineering Co., Ltd.
Taipei, Taiwan

Brazil - Region III

Comercial Importadora Sul Ltda.
(Coimsul)
Rio Grande do Sul, Brazil

Macedo Allison Transmission, Ltda.
Curitiba, Parana, Brazil

Marchao Detroit Allison, Ltda.
Teresina-Piaui, Brazil

Nordeste Comercial Tecnica SA
Salvador, B.A., Brazil

Sao Paulo Detroit Allison S.A.
(Motores e Transmissoes)
Sao Paulo, S.P., Brazil

Tracbel S.A. Engenharia e Comercio
Belo Horizonte, Minas Gerais, Brazil

Asia/Pacific - Region IV

Borneotech, Ltd.
Hua Mark, Bangkok, Thailand

C.I.A.S., Ltd.
Colombo, Sri Lanka

Detroit Engine & Turbine Co.
Bassendean, Western Australia,
Australia

Detroit Engine & Turbine Co.
Altona North, Victoria, Australia

Detroit Engine & Turbine Co.
Sydney, New South Wales, Australia

Detroit Engine & Turbine Co.
Adelaide, South Australia, Australia

Detroit Engine & Turbine Co.
Launceston, Tasmania, Australia

Detroit Engine & Turbine Co.
Darwin, Northern Territory, Australia

Detroit Engine & Turbine Co.
Richlands, Queensland, Australia

Diesel Equipment Distributors, Ltd.
Kwai Chung, Hong Kong

General Diesel Power Corporation
Makati, Metro Manila, Philippines

P.T. Garuda Power Equipment
Jakarta, Indonesia

Pacific Power (Singapore) Private Ltd.
Singapore

Prem Nath Diesels Pvt. Ltd.
New Delhi, India

Latin America/Mexico - Region V

Camtral, S.A.
Buenos Aires, Argentina

Diesel De Puerto Rico, Inc.
Carolina, Puerto Rico

Diesel Power Services, Ltd.
Otaheite, Trinidad, West Indies

General Power Ltd.
Montevideo, Uruguay

Iceta Hnos. S.R.L.
Cordora, Argentina

Impulsora Motriz de Guadalajara,
S.A. de C.V.
Guadalajara, Jalisco, Mexico

Jaras, S.A.
Santiago, Region Metropolitana, Chile

Manuel Salqueiro S.A.
Buenos Aires, Argentina

Maquinaria Igsa, Sa De C.V.
Del. Cuajimapla, Mexico

Motores Y Partes Diesel del Noroeste
S.A. de C.V. (Mopasa)
Hermosillo, Sonora, Mexico

Motores, S.A.
Bogota, Colombia

Recordmotor, S.A.
Quito, Ecuador

Repuestos Diesel, S.A. (Redisa)
Lima 1, Peru

Servi-Fuerza DDA S.A. de C.V.
Chihuahua, Mexico

Stewart & Stevenson De Venezuela,
S.A.
Marcaibo, Venezuela

Transmissiones Refacciones y Motores,
S.A. (Tremosa)
Monterrey, Nuevo Leon, Mexico

Allison Management

1915-1928	James A. Allison, President Speedway Team Company 1915 Allison Experimental Company 1917 Allison Engineering Company 1920
1929	Edward V. Rickenbacker, President Allison Engineering Company, under Fisher & Company
1929-1936	Norman H. Gilman, President and General Manager Allison Engineering Company 1929 Allison Division of General Motors Corporation 1934
1937-1940	Otto T. "Pop" Kreusser, General Manager Allison Division
1940-1942	Fred C. Kroeger, General Manager Allison Division
1942-1943	Cy Osborn, General Manager, Allison Division Vice President, General Motors Corporation
1943-1960	Edward B. Newill, General Manager Allison Division Vice President, General Motors Corporation
1960-1967	Harold H. Dice, General Manager Allison Division Vice President, General Motors Corporation
1965-1967	James E. Knott, Manager of Indianapolis Plants Allison Division
1967-1970	Reuben R. Jensen, General Manager Allison Division Vice President, General Motors Corporation
1970-1978	James E. Knott, General Manager Detroit Diesel Allison Division Vice President, General Motors Corporation
1978-1981	Donald J. Atwood, General Manager Detroit Diesel Allison Division Vice President, General Motors Corporation
1981-1982	Harold L. Smith, General Manager Detroit Diesel Allison Division Vice President, General Motors Corporation
1982-1983	Ludvik F. Koci, General Manager Detroit Diesel Allison Division Vice President, General Motors Corporation
1983-Present	F. Blake Wallace, General Manager Allison Gas Turbine Division Vice President, General Motors Corporation
1987-Present	Robert M. Clark, General Manager Allison Transmission Division

General Index

Cover and Endpapers

The cover and endpapers are original paintings executed for the Allison 75th Anniversary by distinguished American illustrator James Dietz. The cover reflects the division's contemporary era, highlighting the transmissions that have set an industry's standard for off-highway vehicles, military tracked and wheeled equipment, and on-highway trucks and buses of every kind worldwide. Represented, too, are some of the diverse applications in which Allison's torque converters, gear trains, and automatics have made significant contributions.

The front endpaper recalls founder Jim Allison and his company's early job shop days of Indy racing, Liberty engines, and the Gilman bearing. The back endpaper evokes the company's contribution to Allied victory in WWII—the superb powerplant of Warhawks and Airacobras, Lightnings and Mustangs—the V1710 engine. Included are early Allison entries into the turbojet business—the J33s and J35s for Shooting Stars, Scorpions, and Thunderjets—that set world standards for jet engine performance and reliability.

About the Authors

Paul Sonnenburg, born in Duluth, Minnesota, and educated at the University of Southern California, began writing about aero engines as a maintenance planner with Northeast Airlines in Washington, D.C., 30 years ago. After a tour with the U.S. Army in Alaska, Paul served in administration and public relations with TWA and Air-India in New York City. He worked with the Los Angeles Community Colleges in establishing their overseas education programs for the armed services. A director of the Los Angeles City College Foundation, for eight years Paul was a division manager and consultant for an international publisher of regional history books.

William Schoneberger, author and co-author of three aviation and aerospace industry history books, has reported, participated in, and chronicled three decades of aviation and aerospace milestone events. Since 1979 he has operated William A. Schoneberger Communications, specializing in public relations counsel, representation, and writing. A Cincinnati native, Bill graduated from the University of South Carolina and also attended Miami University (Ohio) and the University of Cincinnati. Presently preparing a biography of John K. Northrop, Bill is contributing editor for a major airline trade magazine, president of the Aero Club of Southern California, and Western regional director of the Aviation/Space Writers Association. Bill Schoneberger's book credits include 1980's award-winning *Seven Decades of Progress,* a history of the General Electric Corporation's gas turbine operations; and the 1986 *Out of Thin Air,* a history of the Garrett Corporation (with Robert R.H. Scholl).

Bill Schoneberger and Paul Sonnenburg collaborated in 1984 on *California Wings: A History of Aviation in the Golden State,* warmly received in the industry and notable as the first single-volume narration of all the major facets of the state's remarkably diverse contributions to aviation and aerospace achievement.

About the Artist

San Francisco native Jim Dietz began his career after graduation from Art Center College of Design in Los Angeles in 1969. His gold medal-winning work has appeared in leading magazines, on book jackets, and in Hollywood films. In addition to gallery showings across the nation, Jim has been honored by exhibitions at the Smithsonian Institution and the San Diego Aero Space Museum. He earned best of show honors at the Experimental Aviation Association Art Show for three of the past four years. Jim Dietz lives in Seattle, Washington.

About the Designer

Book designer Robaire Ream, Colorado-born, Paris-raised, and educated in France and Southern California, has designed more than 150 hardcover books and softcover publications. An accomplished artist in several media, notably pencil and pen-and-ink, Robaire is an assistant art director at the Los Angeles book publishing house, Windsor Publications. From computer textbooks to academic anthologies, Robaire's work is noted for textual clarity and bold use of photographic imagery.

About the Photos

Unless otherwise attributed, photographs and drawings come from the Allison Transmission and Allison Gas Turbine division archives in Indianapolis.